THINKING ABOUT COMPLEXITY

Grasping the Continuum through Criticism and Pluralism

THINKING ABOUT COMPLEXITY

Grasping the Continuum through Criticism and Pluralism

Kurt A. Richardson

EMERGENT™

P U B L I C A T I O N S

Thinking About Complexity
Grasping the Continuum through Criticism and Pluralism
Written by: Kurt A. Richardson

Library of Congress Control Number:
    2010926264

ISBN: 978-0-9842164-5-1

Printed in the United States of America

The image on the front cover is a snap shot of a particular cellular automata configuration referred to as Meteor Guns. It was generated using Golly, which is an open source, cross-platform application for exploring Conway's Game of Life and other cellular automata. Golly is freely available at: http://golly.sourceforge.net/.

CONTENTS

```
1   14  ⎫
2   31  ⎪
3   25  ⎬  par 1
4   38  ⎪
5   41  ⎭
6   30
   ─────
   179  W
```

INTRODUCTION

Traditionally the natural sciences, particularly physics, have been regarded as the Gatekeepers of Truth. As such the legitimacy of other forms of knowledge have been suppressed, particularly those methods that characterize the 'softer' sciences, such as sociology, psychology, soft systems, and organization theory for example. This essay begins with a discussion concerning the main features of a complex system, and the nature of the boundaries that emerge within such systems. Subsequent to this discussion, and by assuming that the Universe *at some arbitrarily deep level* can be well-described as a complex system, the essay explores the notion of ontology, or existence, from a complex systems perspective. It is argued that none of the traditional objects of science, or any objects from any discipline, formal or not, can be said to be real *in any absolute sense* although a *substantial realism* may be associated with some of them. Out of this problematization of the concept of 'existence', the limitations of the natural sciences is discussed as well as the deep connection between the 'hard' and the 'soft' sciences.

The basic argument presented concerning the relationship between soft and hard paradigms is that they are both concerned with pattern extraction from abstracted data sets (which extend in both space and time). It is these patterns that form the basis of scientific laws and understanding. The principle difference between the two approaches is that they tolerate different levels of 'noise' in the original data set. In the language of a communications engineer, the two approaches accept different signal-to-noise ratios (SNRs), where the 'signal' is the extracted pattern, and the (so-called) 'noise' is whatever is removed during the extraction process (there is a tendency to regard the resulting signal as somehow more 'real' than the noise even though the applied extraction process is often arbitrarily chosen). Clearly, to suggest that there are two ways (hard and soft) is a gross oversimplification.

In this essay these labels are used loosely to represent two 'fuzzy' regions in a notional 'boundary-stability' continuum. The 'hard' region includes those methods (primarily from the natural sciences) that work effectively with data sets that—after an abstraction process—yield stable reproducible laws that can be used to predict future behavior in a precise manner. In this region it is often possible to choose one abstraction over all others, or at least privilege a certain set of abstractions.

The 'soft' region, on the other hand, includes those methods (primarily from the social and human sciences) that are designed to cope with the inherent ambiguity of the abstraction process for data sets that do not easily yield to a dominant abstraction (and where personal preferences and value judgments can play a central role in methodological choice—although this certainly isn't completely absent in the 'hard' region—even the lofty physical sciences are affected by politicization). In these situations, there are often many potentially overlapping—and potentially contradictory—abstractions that seem equally plausible (leading to the significance of multi-paradigmatic approaches in the social sciences for example).

We might say that the 'hard' region represents situations where the data is merely complicated (or can be reasonably assumed to be so), whereas the 'soft' region represents situations where the data is genuinely complex (in the nonlinear dynamical sense). The numerous methodologies that fall into these two broad (overlapping) categories lead to various levels of understanding that tolerate various levels of SNR depending upon the data set (and therefore data collection approach) utilized. Although it may appear that I am generating support for some kind of 'context type vs. method choice' matrix here (akin to the *system of systems methodologies* in soft systems thinking), I am not. Any method has the potential to shed some light in any context of interest *if* applied in a critical fashion. The importance of being able to determine to some degree where on the 'boundary-stability' continuum the context of interest lies, is that this has implications for how we might utilize the understanding derived from the application of our chosen method. In a sense, it gives us a feel for the risk associated in believing our understanding to be True (with a capital 'T')—it is a 'measure' of the efficacy of our supposed knowledge (the difference between knowledge and understanding I am using here is degree of humility; knowledge is understanding with all the caveats removed).

Beyond the 'soft' region the SNR is so low that practical knowledge is very difficult (if not impossible) to come by. This leads to the question of whether any knowledge of one-off events is indeed possible, or whether there are limits to knowledge when understanding of the 'whole', and how it changes over time, are necessary for progress to be made.

Along the way, the notion of 'intrinsic emergence' will be introduced to block the path to a *localized* 'anything goes' radical relativism.

The aim of this essay, then, will be to describe a general philosophy of complexity, and place complexity science in context. Although, be warned, a general theory of everything often provides very little in the way of useful detail. As the systems scientist Kenneth Boulding remarked more than 50 years ago when considering the idea of a general theory of systems, "[such] a theory would be almost without content, for we always pay for generality by sacrificing content, and all we can say about practically everything is almost nothing," (Boulding, 1956: 197). So in a sense, following Boulding, this essay might be regarding as little more than a complex systems argument for adopting an epistemological position that contains nothing. Although, it is hoped that embracing 'nothing' actually leads to many considerable 'somethings'.

Realism versus Constructivism

There are at least two broad perspectives from which the status of our scientific knowledge claims can be understood. The first is a purely realist view of scientific knowledge, referred to as *scientific realism*. According to this view the "theoretical entities that are characterized by a true theory actually exist even though they cannot be directly observed. Alternatively, that the evidence that confirms a theory also serves to confirm the existence of any theoretical or 'hypothetical' entities characterized by that theory" (Fetzer & Almeder, 1993: 118). This definition suggests that scientific knowledge gives us *direct* knowledge of entities that exist independent of the existence of any observer, i.e., rigorous application of scientific methods yields theories of certain entities that exist mind-independently (independently of what we believe or feel about those entities). In this view an objective reality does exist, and as Francis Bacon pointed out in 1620 in his *Novum Organum*, it is through the application of method that we can escape our physiological, psychological, sociological and linguistic biases and acquire objective scientific knowledge of 'reality'.

In complete opposition to the realist position is idealism. This position argues that, although there may exist an objective reality, we can never have direct objective knowledge of that reality. Accordingly, knowledge is totally manufactured rather than discovered. The manufacturing process is inherently biased by our methods of production and is incapable of delivering objective knowledge of some external reality: objectivity is reduced to myth, or wishful thinking. Social constructivism, which is a form of idealism, in its extreme form

5

regards scientific knowledge as merely a socially-constructed discourse that is inherently subjective in nature. As there can be no objective knowledge, there can be no dominant discourse because there can be no test or argument that could conclusively support the dominance of one discourse over another. As such, science is just one approach from many for making sense, and should be treated with no more reverence than any other approach.

The Relationship between Language and Objective Reality

An alternative way to distinguish between realism and idealism is to consider the relationship between the language we use to *describe* reality and reality itself. Realists argue that there is a one-to-one correspondence between our language and 'reality'. This leads to a number of interesting consequences like, for example, the belief that there is a best, or universal, language for describing reality and that, that language happens to be the language of science, namely mathematics and logic.

Idealists, specifically relativists, on the other hand argue that there is no relationship whatsoever between our language and reality. The terms or labels we use are no more than useful sense-making tools that, though convenient, have no intrinsic basis in a hypothetical objective reality.

Although I do not believe that anyone who supports either of these positions is naïve enough to believe in them wholeheartedly, this is generally how the debate between realism and idealism is set up. Physical scientists are criticized for their intellectual arrogance/imperialism, which is justified through strongly realist beliefs, and idealist critics are ridiculed for their apparently wild and poorly argued descriptions of what they think science actually is, as well as their omission of 'reality' in their theories.

The Dominance of the Physical Sciences

Primarily because of the success of science-driven technology there is an enormous wealth of a certain type of evidence that supports the privileging of scientific discourse over every other. This success has perhaps blinded us to the shortcomings of the scientific process, and has lead to an unquestioned belief that because science has successfully explained so much it can probably explain everything. Every facet of human life can supposedly be productively examined through the eyes of science. This position is commonly referred to as scientism (although practical science—as opposed to some popularized caricatures of science—is not synonymous with scientism). And, although indirect evidence of these shortcomings is becoming more widespread, putting the brakes on the train of scientism is no trivial undertaking. Too often the failures of science, which are considerable when we consider social planning or environmental policy, are put down to the bad application of scientific methods rather than seeing these failures as the result of applying scientific methods to inappropriate subject matter.

7

Contrary to popular belief science is not capable of considering all phenomena. In fact, it is quite inflexible in its requirements. The principle requirement that will be considered herein is that scientific methods require that the object of interest is stable, i.e., the boundaries (or, patterns) that delimit the object from the 'background' (the object's complement) must be stable and assumed to be *real*. This stability allows repetitive examinations to be undertaken that allow the knowledge concerning that object to be refined and tested, so much so, that our confidence in our knowledge of that object becomes so great that we might begin to unquestionably assume that we have an accurate (or, absolute) description to hand. In a more generic way, what I am saying is that scientific knowledge can only be obtained for contexts which are incredibly stable. This approach yields a tremendous amount of practical understanding that can be turned to the development of cars, computers, building methods, etc.—just about anything that can be constructed from parts that behave qualitatively in much the same way whatever context they are placed within. What about the objects of interest that have far less rigid boundaries? Social systems for example change and evolve. The boundaries, or patterns, that describe such systems continuously change and emerge, such that the extraction of uniformities is far from a trivial matter. By their very nature the context changes and repetitive examinations are at worse impossible, and at best highly problematic. To apply science to such systems we have to enforce stability. We are forced to reduce the system of interest to an idealized caricature that remains steady over a certain period of time. Of course this is what we really do when we look at any system, be it an atom or an ecology, but for some reason our reductions seem to be more harmful when considering ecologies (i.e., complex systems) as the differences between a description that would allow a scientific analysis, and a notional 'real' description, are huge.

These cracks in the scientific façade have been made more apparent with our ability, supported through incredible growth in computer power (and, ironically, through the dogmatic application of reductionist science) to construct models of simple[1] complex systems. The emerging science of complexity directs us to revisit the nature of scientific knowledge, and at the same time presents us with an alternative approach to understanding the limits of scientific, or more specifically reductionist, methods. The interest for me personally is that, though many criticisms of science have been made by those whom the scientific community has regarded as outsiders and non-scientists, complexity science leads to a critique of science couched in the language of science itself. In a sense, the scientific language contains within it the clear evidence of its own limitations.

_____

1. The concept 'simple complex system' may seem contradictory, but what I am trying to emphasize is that the models we create of complex systems are still very much simplifications of what actually is. We are capable of modelling/representing only the simplest aspects of complex systems.

EXPLORING COMPLEX SYSTEMS

What is a Complex System?

A complex system is comprised of a large number of non-linearly interacting non-decomposable elements.

This is the simple definition of a complex system that is often used, in various forms, and is very similar to Langefors (1995: 55) definition of a general system:

A system is a set of entities with relations between them.

or, Van Gigch's (1991: 30) definition:

A system is an assembly or set of related elements.

If 'nonlinearly' is inserted before "related elements" then we end up with a very similar definition to the one given at the beginning of this essay. As Backlund (2000) has pointed out these sorts of definitions are incomplete. To ensure that the system we are interested in may not be simply reduced to multiple non-interacting subsystems then we must also add that *the systems' components are connected in a way that prevents our system of interest being reduced to two or more distinct systems[2].*

_____

2. As such a system evolves there may will be times when

In addition to this particular shortcoming, the connectivity of the system must be such that the system displays behaviors associated with complex systems before it can be labeled as such. For example, as we shall discuss in the next section, complex systems display emergent properties, as there exists a non-trivial relationship between the system components and the systems macroscopic properties. In my past endeavors to understand complex systems I have tried to develop, on a number of occasions, a typology that would clearly distinguish between complex and complicated systems; one that would hold up to scrutiny. One particular way of doing this is to regard complicated systems as much the same as complex systems except not having sufficient connectivity to display complex behaviors, such as emergence. However, when trying to conceive of a boundary between these two categories one quickly finds that it is very hard indeed, if not impossible, to develop a sound division that could be applied in all cases. What I quickly came to conclude was that the division between complicated and complex depended critically upon how the system was connected. Depending upon how the complicated system was put together, it may be the case that only a few additional connections would be sufficient to transform it into a complex system, for example.

---

the system can be approximated as multiple weakly interacting (sub)systems. However, such a state is often only temporary and so the validity (or usefulness) of any understanding derived through the application of such assumptions would also be temporary.

It should be noted that the complicated/complex distinction is not equivalent to the commonly used linear/non-linear distinction. Complicated systems may contain many non-linear interactions (e.g., computers are commonly regarding as examples of linear systems despite the fact that they comprise a vast number of non-linear responsive components such as transistors), they may even display limited non-linear behaviors. The key difference between the two is the absence of (apparent) 'novelty' in complicated systems[3]. Complex systems can emerge into states that are not readily apparent from their constitution—in a sense new states are created[4].

The principle difference between complicated and complex system is the presence of causal loops. For a system to be complex it must be connected in such a way that multiple causal loops are present that themselves interact with each other. So it is the qualitative structure of the connectivity that supports, or not, complex behaviors. But again, the determination of a qualitative universal design process is problematic, and to my mind, an impossible undertaking in any complete sense. I be-

---

3. The usage of 'novelty' here refers only to our inability to completely understand a complex system—it is a reflection of our ignorance, not of some mystical process of creation.

4. These states are coded in the microscopic description—we just do not yet know how to decode the macro from the micro. The distinction between micro and macro and the recognition of emergent products are discussed at length in Richardson (2004a).

lieve that the best we can hope for is a method that would allow investigators to identify the causal loops that are primarily responsible for enabling complex behavior, for a particular system only[5]. From this, investigators could identify ways in which the system could be manipulated to be complicated or complex. But, it is important to bear in mind that such tests would only work for idealized and well-described systems. The benefits that such a test would bring to our understanding of real life systems are not at all clear cut. The difficulties confronting the design of such a testing apparatus will become clear as the essay progresses. For more detail on the behavioral and structural differences between complicated and complex systems please refer to Richardson (2007).

From this brief discussion of the definitions it is clear that they are insufficient (after all, the notion of incompressibility explicitly denies the completeness of any definition—Richardson, Cilliers & Lissack, 2001). In an attempt to address these shortfalls we might rewrite the initial definition of a complex system as:

A complex system is comprised of a large number of non-linearly interacting non-decomposable elements. The interactivity must be such that the system cannot be reducible to two or more distinct systems, and must contain a sufficiently complex interactive mixture of causal loops to allow the system to display the behav-

---

5. Richardson (2005, 2007, 2009) reports on the relationship between structure and behavior in complex non-linear dynamical systems.

iors characteristic of such systems (where the determination of "sufficiently" is problematic)[6].

A rather circular definition possibly? A complex system is a (topologically complex) system that displays complex behavior! Despite its circularity, which highlights the problematic nature of defining complex systems, this will be the 'description' assumed from here on.

Complex System's Behavior

Complex systems as described above display some very interesting well-popularized behaviors. The two most dominating 'forces' within a complex system are the forces that push the system towards chaotic behavior, and those that encourage self-organization (anti-chaos): a struggle between disorder and order, if you like, much akin to Anaximander's notion of elements in conflict ("They 'pay penalty and retribution to each other for their injustice according to the assessment of Time'", Gottlieb, 2000: 9). I tend to argue that despite this apparent tension chaos is actually a result of self-organization, i.e., a complex system can self-

---

6. Of course this is an idealization. In real world complex systems, making the assumption of non-decomposable elements, for example, is a major simplifying step. Also, if we look hard enough we can always find further connections that will force us to limit our system description arbitrarily. As a result, we are always forced to make a judgment as to what connections are significant or not in developing our system boundaries—this is a non-trivial exercise.

organize into a structure that leads to a chaotic mode of behavior (hinting perhaps at the possibility of higher-order parameters); it does not, therefore, follow that self-organization leads to some kind of preferential order.

In previous articles (see Cilliers, 1998; Richardson *et al.*, 2009, for example) it has been suggested that complex systems at least display the following characteristics:

1. Their current behavior depends upon their history;
2. They display a wide-range of qualitatively different behaviors;
3. As already mentioned, the system's evolution can be incredibly sensitive to small changes as well as being incredibly resilient to large change (and all combinations in between);
4. Complex systems are incompressible, i.e., it is impossible to have an account of a complex system which will predict all possible system behaviors[7].

System History

In Richardson *et al.* (2009) it was argued that a key distinction between complex and complicated systems was that history was of more importance when considering complex systems than it is for complicated systems. The example given as a complicated system was a silicon-

---

7. This aspect of complexity was the focus of a previous paper which argues for critical pluralism in the management sciences, Richardson, Cilliers & Lissack (2001).

based computer, and a social system was given as an example of a complex system. I feel that some comment concerning the role of history as an analytical tool is necessary. The main difference between these two examples is that, for a computer, it is more or less a straightforward issue to determine what its current state is. History as an analytical tool is less important in this case because an analyst could easily account for history's affect on the computer by *directly* examining its current state, or configuration (e.g., what software it is currently running).

However, if we take a social system it is nigh on impossible to get such an accurate appreciation of its current state. If we could view its current state directly its future evolution would be quite easy to ascertain (although difficulties associated with non-linearity would still place significant limits on our predictive powers). However, we cannot ever know the current state of each comprising individual (which would require a comprehensive understanding of their current epistemic state that would allow us to predict, albeit in a limited way, how each person would respond to particular stimuli) and the detailed form of the interrelationships. So, to obtain a clearer picture, or even a very basic picture, of the current state we can examine the system's history to indirectly develop an appreciation of what the current state of the system is, thus allowing an informed, though very approximate, prediction to be made about its future. History as an analytical tool is important simply because complex systems are often too opaque to the eyes of the observer; whereas direct observation yields a very accurate picture of a complicated system, such approaches yield little when considering complex systems and so indirect historical methods can be very useful indeed. However, the interpretation of historical data or texts is always open to question, so an appreciation of the current state of a social system based upon its past behavior is always incomplete and bias. It follows that any predictions made from a historical 'model' will also be incomplete and biased.

The role of indirect historical evidence in the development of a clear understanding of the current state of a complex system does not replace the role of direct observational evidence. The argument is simply that history, as an analytical tool, offers another route to the understanding of complex systems over and above that offered by direct methods, whereas for complicated systems a historical analysis would offer little (unless of course you are interested in the overall evolution of computer design (which would be a complex system) rather than the functioning of one particular computer).

Qualitatively Different Behaviors and Scale Independence

As already suggested herein and elsewhere (see Allen, 2001 for example), complex systems display a rich variety of qualitatively different behavioral regimes. This phenomena is scale-independent, i.e., the possible qualitatively different behaviors that one might observe depend upon the scale, or level, one is observing. For example, and it is an extreme example, if one could view a social system down at the level of individual quarks (almost, say, at the 'bitmap' level of reality) it would be hard, if not impossible, to recognize the qualitatively different behaviors that manifest at the human scale. So the natural (it seems) emergence of (quasi-) hierarchical levels helps considerably when trying to understand complex systems (a topic that will recur throughout this essay).

If one attempted to draw a (snapshot of a) phase space portrait (i.e., a behavior space representation) of a complex system, it would only be a representation of the possibilities that might occur at one particular level of aggregation/abstraction. Not only will different phase portraits exist at different levels of aggregation/abstraction, but as the different levels interact with each other (which again is scale-independent) the phase variables (also called order parameters) that are relevant for the construction of a particular phase portrait at a particular level will change, i.e., different phase variables might best reflect the current state and future possibilities of the system than ones that might have previously characterized the system. Not only does the quantitative nature of the state variables change, but the qualitative nature changes also.

The existence of (quasi-) levels, which we shall return to, certainly facilitates the development of understanding for a complex system. It has been suggested that each level displays a *substantial realism* (Emmeche, *et al.*, 2000), meaning that there exist robust representations of aspects of complex systems that need not include the whole system—an argument for some kind of soft reductionism perhaps. I think that this is a very important point as much of the complexity writings I have come across generally trivialize the process by which it is decided whether or not a particular system is complex, or can be legitimately treated as such. It is also rarely acknowledged that even a complex systems description is still a bounded description—an idealization—and therefore still very much reductionistic in nature.

Chaos versus Anti-Chaos

The perturbations that might cause a reaction within a complex system of interest come from without that system. This is an important point. When analysts build models of organizations, for example, the key implicit assumption that is made is that the decision-maker is outside of the organization of interest, i.e., a subject-object dualism is implicitly maintained. Analysts, consultants, decision-makers, etc., look at the system of interest, attempt to understand its current state, and use the resulting model to make predictions that support a particular course of action. In this approach, the analyst decision-maker (etc.) is assumed to be outside the system looking-in, trying to push it in a particular direction. Change can come, by definition, from two general quarters: from within or from without. Change from within is emergent and often inevitable if perturbations from the outside do not act to affect (via changing component relationships) the emergent process. Change from without comes as a reaction to these external perturbations.

Whether change comes from within or from without, the overall change to the system is problematic to determine. The system's behavior might be radically affected, or the system might absorb any attempt to change and continue on its current path relatively unaffected. Though, it is important to remember that attempts to change the system (failed or not) may result in delayed changes despite no apparent immediate reaction. Who knows what chain of events might have been triggered; the seeds for a new possibility might have unintentionally been sown.

This distinction of being 'inside' or 'outside' the system will be revisited again. It certainly raises some interesting issues regarding how useful one can be being 'outside', and the relationship between 'outsider' and 'insider' knowledge.

Furthermore, given that the fundamental assumption of this essay is that there is only one coherent and complete complex system (the Universe), how can we even justify the seemingly innocent assumption that other systems exist that can be treated as such? The belief that systems do in fact exist (such as a particular organization) in interaction with an environment that can be analyzed as such appears on the surface to be such a plainly obvious assumption to make; so obvious in fact that it is rarely considered to be anything more than obvious.

Incompressibility

Bottom-Up Limitations

In Richardson, Cilliers & Lissack (2001) it was argued that incompressibility is the 'showstopper' for a theory of everything, or a comprehensive theory of complexity, and is the key reason in support of a quasi-'critical pluralist' philosophy. However, if we consider a cellular-automata-type experiment (to be defined on p. 51), for example, then it is a trivial matter to have a complete description of such a complex system. How can the importance of the incompressibility of complex systems be maintained if in fact completely describable complex systems do exist and can be easily constructed? In taking the example of the cellular automata experiment in which everything about the *composition* of the complex system is readily known, we can say that complex systems are incompressible in *behavioral* terms but not necessarily in *compositional* terms. So what makes such an idealized complex system otherwise incompressible? The showstopper is (computational) *intractability*, i.e., the inability to predict all future states of the system, despite complete compositional knowledge, without running the system itself. There is no algorithmic shortcut to a *complete* description of the future. Wolfram (1985: 735) suggests that "[c]omputational reducibility may well be the exception rather than the rule," and that for irreducible (incompressible) systems "their own evolution is effectively the most efficient procedure for determining their future" (p. 737). This is very similar to Chaitin's definition for a random number series: "A series of numbers is random if the smallest algorithm capable of specifying it to a computer has about the same number of bits of information as the series itself" (Chaitin, 1975: 48). This seems to imply that incompressibility is very closely related to Chaitin's notion of randomness. Does this mean that if a complex system is incompressible then it is random? In a sense the answer is yes. But, whether a complex system is random or not depends strongly on one's tolerance for noise. If one demands *complete* understanding, then the system of interest needs to be expressed in its entirety and knowledge could only be obtained by running the system itself. However, if one was less stringent in one's toleration of 'noise'[8] then maybe patterns could be found that in a rough and incomplete way would allow for a description to be extracted that would indeed be less than the total description and yet

---

8. Here, like with the notion of 'novelty', we are concerned not with the external influences that cause our idealized model of a particular 'system' to wander off course from its idealized path. Again, it is a measure of our ignorance, not of some mystical forces 'out there'. For example, in Peter Allen's modeling work, noise is often introduced, not because the noise exists in the real world, but to some way represent the impact of the omissions forced upon the modeler as part of the modeling process (modeling essentially is the art and science of reduction after all). The noise is added in an effort to include the effects of everything that was not included in the idealized model. Following Edmunds (2000: 380): "...noise can be seen as that which is unpredictable given the available resources of the modeler. In this way noise is distinguished from randomness."

still contain useful understanding. Again, we will return to this issue later.

An example of the type of incompressibility[9], or intractability, described above can be found in the hierarchy of the sciences (Figure 1). Chemists, for example, provide a description of reality at the molecular and molecular complex level. Physicists traditionally sit below chemistry as being the more fundamental science considering the constituents of molecules, namely, atoms, quarks and maybe superstrings; chemistry supposedly emerges from physics. However, there is a lot more physics in chemistry than physicists actually know about. The ability to bootstrap from physics to chemistry is well beyond current science. The problem is compounded further if we try to bootstrap from chemistry to biology, which deals with cells and multi-cellular entities. As Douglas Hofstadter (1984) remarks in *Gödel, Escher, Bach* "a bootstrap from simple molecules to entire cells is almost beyond one's power to imagine" (p. 548). As we move up the hierarchy, more and more of the 'noise' of (fundamental) reality is omitted. In the absence of a complete bootstrapping method it is simply assumed that the ontology

---

9. We shall see later in the essay, when exploring the Universe as a vast cellular automata experiment, that we need to distinguish between two types of incompressibility that are derived from: 1. Intractability, i.e., the play between order and disorder as well as the loss of 'something' in the aggregation process even if the compositional (idealized) description is complete (as described above), and 2. The fact that all bounded descriptions are incomplete descriptions.

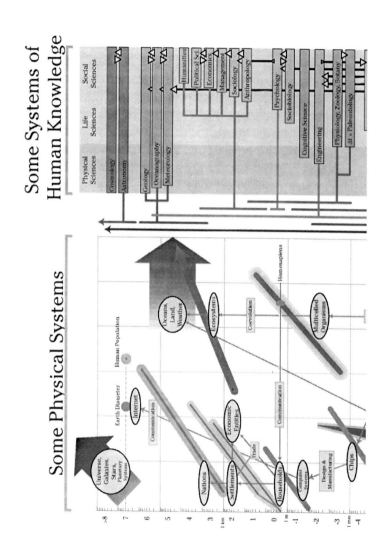

Some Systems of Human Knowledge

Physical Sciences   Life Sciences   Social Sciences

Cosmology
Astronomy
Geology
Oceanography
Meteorology
Humanities
Political Sci.
Economics
Management
Sociology
Anthropology
Psychology
Sociobiology
Cognitive Science
Engineering
Physiology, Zoology, Botany
Mx = Paleontology

Some Physical Systems

Universe, Galaxies, Stars, Planetary Systems
Oceans, Land, Weather
Ecosystems
Coevolution
Homo sapiens
Multicelled Organisms
Internet
Communication
Human Population
Earth Diameter
Economic Entities
Trade
Communication
Nations
Settlements
Households
Computer System
Design & Manufacturing
Chips

>8
7
6
5
4
1 km 3
2
1
0
1 m
-1
-2
1 mm
-3
-4

24

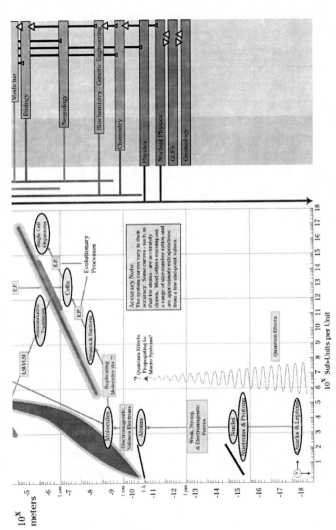

Figure 1 *The reality of hierarchies versus the hierarchy of the natural sciences. (© 2005 Marshall Clemens, www.idiagram.com—used by kind permission)*

25

that each science is based upon is legitimate in itself and that the lower levels can be approximately ignored without too much loss of 'noise'. Bottom-up computer simulations approach their subject matter in more or less the same way. An ontological position is assumed, i.e., the nature and form of the basic building blocks are determined, and the macroscopic behavior that emerges is deemed more life-like because it emerges from a lower-level ontological commitment—on the surface the models look more like reality, so the conclusions must therefore be more robust. But, how secure are their ontological foundations? As with those of the traditional sciences, the strength and basis of these ontological commitments will be explored later. An extended discussion of the nature of hierarchies from a complex systems perspective is offered in Richardson, 2004a.

Top-Down Limitations

Even if we can have complete compositional knowledge of a complex system (observable at the human level of existence) intractability places some severe limitations on our possible behavioral knowledge. What limitations are placed on us if we do not even have good compositional knowledge? We can begin by viewing the system at a higher level. At higher levels we can recognize alternative sets of interacting entities that 'exist' (or are recognizable as such) only at higher levels. For example, it would be utterly pointless to investigate organizations at the level of quarks, but we can make good progress by considering employees to be the fundamental building blocks. It must be remembered, however, that these higher-level entities are emergent aggregates of those 'existing' at a lower level. As such, our higher-level abstractions inherently cannot help but miss something out. These abstractions approximate the complex system by assuming the absolute existence of higher levels, and therefore higher entities, despite the fact that these higher 'beings' emerge from the lower levels—the higher-level existence is assumed to be an emergent property of the level beneath, which is in turn is an emergent property of the level beneath that and so on until the fundamental components (superstrings?) are reached.

Let's assume for a moment that we could speculate as to the nature of the entities and interactions at the level beneath the level we might be interested in (e.g., we might be interested in how an organization functions, so we build an agent-based model that assumes the employees represent the level beneath the organizational level). If we could achieve this then we could construct a model (a computer-based agent model, for example) of the lower (employee) level, which would have as its emergent properties the next higher (organizational) level. We could then speculate as to the composition of the layer below (multicellular?) the lower (employee) level, which would again have as its emergent properties the (employee) layer above. In principle we could continue this process all the way down to the bottom level comprised of the absolutely fundamental components (superstrings?) and re-

27

lationships. However, how could we be sure that at each stage we had selected the correct abstraction? The only supporting evidence we would have would be limited empirical evidence. But, because of the nature of nonlinearity there is a huge number of ways to abstract a (nonlinear) problem in such a way that will easily be confirmed by our limited empirical evidence, i.e., there is one way to 'curve-fit' a linear problem (assuming a fixed number of dimensions) but there is an infinite number of ways to 'curve-fit' a non-linear problem (see Figure 2). So, the idea that agent-based modelers have better models (and therefore more knowledge) than other modelers is simply not the case, as in principle there is an infinite number of microscopic sets (i.e., members of the lower level) that would lead to, in some limiting way, the desired macroscopic properties (i.e., the level above). As such we still cannot be sure that our knowledge is transferable to any other contexts except those already observed. There is no doubt that agent-based modeling (which for most intents and purposes are simply advanced versions of simple cellular automata experiments) is a powerful method for analysis, and the analysts' toolset is significantly enhanced with their inclusion, but we should not get too carried away with the idea that they are somehow better models of reality. Their similarities with 'perceived' reality might run very shallow indeed.[10]

---

10. For a more in-depth discussion of the limitations of bottom-up simulation please refer to Richardson (2008).

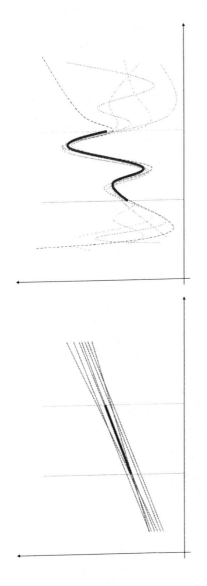

Figure 2 *Linear Versus Non-Linear. In both illustrations the thick line/curve within the two vertical lines represents some set of empirical data for an observed range of contexts. The other lines/curves represent predictive data based on different possible theoretical explanations for those empirical data, and extend beyond contexts for which such empirical data exists. The figures illustrate the difficulties in extending current explanations, or theories, of known contexts to new, as yet unobserved, contexts.*

So back to our basic question: "how do we know we've chosen the right abstraction?" The short answer is that "we can't." But this isn't a showstopper by any means for analysis, science, or any intellectual endeavor.

In summary, the limits to understanding complex systems come not only from our inability to bootstrap from one level to another in either direction, but also from the fact that the only *complete* description (if that is what we demand) must be constructed from absolutely the bottom-up (e.g., from universal superstrings upwards) rather than from the top, or middle, down. This does not deny the possibility of developing useful and relatively robust knowledge from starting points other than the consideration of everything (see, e.g., Richardson, 2005). In a simple cellular automata experiment, for which perfect compositional knowledge is known, the future development can only be determined *fully* if the model itself is run. If we start with limited knowledge of some future development we can never be sure that a model obtained by working backwards will be accurate; we must have *complete* knowledge to build a *complete* model—a theoretical as well as a practical impossibility.

We will revisit this topic when we come to consider the Universe as such a cellular automata experiment and the limits of scientific knowledge, as well as all other forms of knowledge.

In the argument presented thus far, there has been an undercurrent flowing concerning the nature of boundaries, i.e., the ontological

30

status of boundaries, structures or patterns. Further exploration of the nature of boundaries, and therefore the ontological status of 'objects' or 'entities', will be the foundation from which an evolutionary philosophy will be constructed and legitimized.

THE ONTOLOGICAL STATUS
OF BOUNDARIES

This section will discuss the nature of boundaries in a complex system, or the ontological status of 'objects'/'entities'. Initially the nature of boundaries from a spatio-temporal perspective will be discussed first, followed by an exploration of the boundary concept from a phase space perspective. These two perspectives will then be used to argue for a position in which no boundaries really exist in a complex system (except those defining its comprising components), but that a distribution of boundary (structure) stabilities does exist which legitimates a wide range of paradigmatically different analytical approaches (without the rejection of natural science methods). However, in this part of the analysis assumptions are made about the efficacy of variables and their non-linear interrelationships that are not necessarily justified. In what seems to be a back-to-front way, the second part of this section will briefly consider how it is that we can even make such claims about the relationship between modelled boundaries and natural boundaries. The discussion here will be brief, as it will be expanded upon in the section that considers the Universe as a vast cellular automata experiment. I also hope that the choice of presenting these ideas in a seemingly back-to-front manner will also become clear.

Emerging Domains

If one were to view the spatio-temporal evolution of an idealized complex system, one would observe that different structures, or patterns, wax and wane. In complex systems, different domains can emerge that might even display qualitatively different behaviors from their neighboring domains. A domain is simply defined herein as an apparently autonomous (possibly critically-organized) structure that differentiates itself from the whole (i.e., it stands out from the 'noise'). The apparent autonomy is illusory though. All domains (patterns) are emergent structures that persist for undecideably different durations. A particular domain, or structure or subsystem, may seem to appear spontaneously, persist for a long period and then fade away. Particular organizations or industries can be seen as emergent domains that are apparently self-sustaining and separate from other organizations or industries.

Figure 3 illustrates the spontaneous emergence of order in a simple complex system (the mathematical details of which are not relevant for this discussion). Different domains emerge whose 'edges', or boundaries, change and evolve as the system evolves. Though a snapshot of the system's evolution would show clear structures, it would be wrong to assume that such structures were a permanent and *real* feature of the system; the structures are emergent and temporary.

Although it is argued here that all boundaries are emergent and temporary, some boundaries may persist for very long periods. For

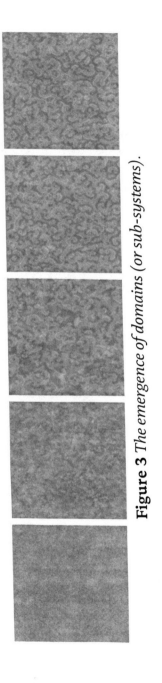

Figure 3 *The emergence of domains (or sub-systems).*

example, the boundaries that delimit a proton (which is arguably an emergent manifestation of the combined interactive behavior of quarks, or superstrings) from its complement, persist for periods theorized to be longer than the current age of the Universe (possibly $> 10^{33}$ s), after which the boundaries decay (through the emission of an X particle) and a new set of boundaries emerge (a positron and a pion, which then decay into three electromagnetic showers). Not all boundaries are so persistent and predictable in their evolution. The boundaries that describe an eddy current in a turbulent fluid (which could be seen as the emergent property of the liquid's constituent molecules) are short-lived. Most boundaries of interest in our daily lives exist somewhere in between these two extremes. The boundaries that define the organizations we work within, those (conceptual) boundaries that define the context(s) for meaning, the boundaries that define ourselves (both physically and physiologically) are generally quite stable with low occurrences of significant qualitative change, although quantitative change is ubiquitous.

It is also important to remember that the observation of domains, and their defining boundaries, depends upon the scale, or level, one is interested in (which is often related to what one wants to achieve, i.e., ones purpose).

An example of persistent boundaries and resulting levels again comes from the natural sciences, which has obvious direct connections with the hierarchy of sciences discussed earlier. The hierarchy of quarks □ bosons & fermions

☐ atoms ☐ molecules ☐ cells ☐ etc. is very resilient. Choosing which level to base our explanations within is no easy task, particularly as any selection will be deficient in some way or another (refer back to the discussion on top-down or bottom-up representation).

At the level of quarks (even if we could directly observe that level), say, it would be difficult to distinguish between two people, though at the molecular level this becomes much easier, and at the human level the task seems trivial (though we are increasingly at risk of believing what we *see* is what there *is* simply out of habit). The level taken to make sense of a system depends upon the accuracy required or the practically achievable. Organizations (economic domains or subsystems) are very difficult, if not impossible, to understand in terms of individuals so they are often described as coherent systems in themselves with the whole only being assumed to *exist*[11].

In short, the recognition of boundaries is problematic and is related to the level of aggregation (scale) we choose to view.

Evolutionary Phase Spaces

The emergent domain aspect of complex systems is complexified further when the behaviors of different domains are included. Let's assume for the moment that we are interested in a particularly stable domain—a particular orga-

11. The general unhappiness of the modern employee is a testament to the dangers of over simplifying this particular organizational problem.

nization for example. We might perform some kind of analysis, a cluster analysis for example, that allows us to extract or infer, in a *rough and incomplete* way, a number of order parameters (i.e., parameters that when changed, change the domain's behavior) and their interrelationships that seem to characterize the observed domain's behavior. We can then draw a picture of the domain's phase space, which will provide information regarding the qualitatively different modes of behavior of that domain for varying time. Figure 4 shows the evolution of such a phase space for a very simple idealized nonlinear system. The two main variables are position (y-axis) and velocity (x-axis) and the two dominant shades represent the two main attractors for this system (black represents an unstable equilibrium attractor). So on the first snapshot (taken at time = 0), depending on what the initial values of the order parameters are, the system is either attracted to the attractor represented by the light grey or the attractor represented by the dark grey.

The proceeding snapshots show how the phase space evolves with the two qualitatively different attractor spaces mixing more and more as time wears on. What we find for this particular system is that, though we know that there are two distinct attractors, after a relatively short period the two attractor spaces are mixed at a very low level of detail indeed. In fact the pattern quickly becomes fractal, meaning that we require infinite detail to know what qualitative state the system will be in. Even with qualitatively stable order parameters

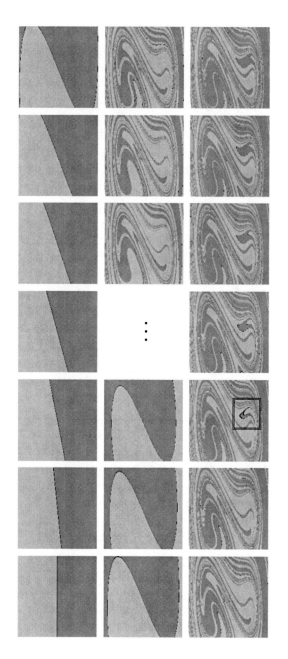

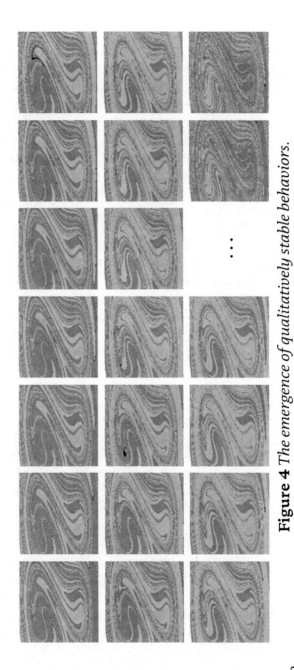

Figure 4 *The emergence of qualitatively stable behaviors.*

qualitatively unstable behavior occurs (see for example Kan, 1994). These are referred to as 'riddled states', or 'riddled basins of attraction' (Sommerer & Ott, 1993).

Despite this continuous mixing of states, stable areas of phase space *do* emerge and persist. Figure 4 shows an example of this by highlighting the emergence of a stable region that persists to the end of the modeled evolution. This is of interest because it demonstrates that not only is quantitative prediction problematic, but that qualitative prediction is also problematic (as opposed to being impossible). But remember that the example given is for a stable domain with qualitatively stable order parameters. For a domain, that is an emergent property of a complex system having other emergent neighbors, the order parameters will not necessarily be qualitatively stable. The defining order parameters might be *qualitatively unstable*. (This demonstrates that the order parameters are simply trends that offer a superficial (though often useful) and temporary understanding of any real system of interest.) The evolution of these phase variables will depend upon the interaction between the neighboring domains, which is a manifestation of causal processes at the lower levels (an argument for meta-order parameters perhaps). This introduces nontrivial difficulties for any observer's attempts to make sense, i.e., derive robust knowledge. The fact that such change is not random, with the existence of stable structures as well as behaviors, means that the possibility of deriving useful understanding is not wholly undermined.

Before moving on to briefly consider simple cellular automata and Conway's *Game of Life*, a terminological link must be made between the above discussion on boundaries/domains and 'objects'/'entities' if it is not already apparent. Domains *are* 'objects' or 'entities'. In this analysis a proton, a tree, a car, a nation state, are legitimate objects that are identified as being persistent and apparently autonomous phase space (as well as spatio-temporal, which is how they are ordinarily recognized) domains or patterns. But, and it is an important but, how can we justify not only this leap from persistent structures to everyday objects, but also that phase variables or order parameters should have any basis in the real world at all? This directly addresses the issue of whether mathematics, or any structured language, has any rights at all in claiming that it can be used to represent 'reality'. To explore this concern we turn to cellular automata—the simplest form of all possible complex systems.

CELLULAR AUTOMATA AND QUASI-ENTITY DYNAMICS

Before exploring the implications of assuming a cellular automaton (CA) Universe this section will present some of the key characteristics of CA systems and present some of the findings derived from the growing field of computational mechanics.

Cellular Automata Explained

For the purposes of this essay I will not detail the construction of cellular automata. The interested reader is encouraged to read Hanson and Crutchfield (1997). A lighter introduction is offered by Poundstone (1985), and to stand any chance of really appreciating the upcoming distinction between BMP and JPEG descriptions of reality, you really must play with CAS yourself. *Golly* is an open source, cross-platform application for exploring Conway's *Game of Life* and other cellular automata. It is free, easy to use, and the philosophical insights that can be extracted from playing with Golly cannot be underestimated—download it from golly. sourceforge.net. Here I offer a minimal mathematical description.

In introducing CA I will make use of the notation used by Hanson and Crutchfield (1997). The *state* or *configuration* of a CA at a time t is denoted by S_t and consists of a one-dimensional array of sites $\{i = 0,..., N\text{-}1\}$ where N is the size of the CA network. Each site has a value s_t^i which is chosen from a finite alphabet $A = \{0, 1,..., k\text{-}1\}$, so $S_t \in A^N$. In the case of elementary

CAS considered herein the alphabet consists of only two states, 0 and 1, so $A = \{0, 1\}$; all *words* and *sentences*, or configurations, must be constructed from this simple alphabet. The *local site-update function* φ which operates on *neighborhoods* $\eta_t^i = s_t^{i-r}...s_t^i...s_t^{i+r}$ of radius r is written $s_{t+1}^i = \varphi(\eta_t^i)$. The list of all neighborhoods η and their corresponding outputs $\varphi(\eta)$ comprise the CAS *lookup table*. Again, we only consider very simple CAS in this essay with neighborhood radii, $r = 1$. An example of a complete lookup table for such an elementary CA might be:

$$\Phi(\eta) = \begin{cases} 0, \eta \to \{111,110,011,000\} \\ 1, \eta \to \{101,100,010,001\} \end{cases}$$

which is the case for elementary CA 54. The *global update operator*, or the *ensemble evolution operator*, $\Phi: A^N \longrightarrow A^N$ is applied in parallel to all neighborhoods in the array. So, for this elementary system we can define the equation of motion as $\mathbf{S}_{t+1} = \Phi(\mathbf{S}_t)$ which effectively creates new *words* and *sentences* from the finite alphabet A. This is the fundamental 'Law of Physics' or 'Theory of Everything' for such systems.

In a cellular automata world every 'atom' is described and accounted for. No shortcuts are taken to approximate the CA's overall behavior—everything is described and modelled in exact detail. Figure 5a shows the evolution of a particular 1-dimensional CA world. The first line in the image depicts the starting configuration—every point, atom, or pixel in that world is described completely. Each subsequent line

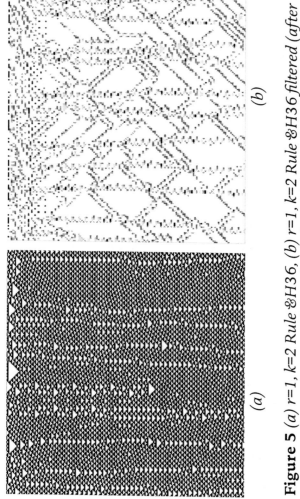

Figure 5 *(a) r=1, k=2 Rule &H36, (b) r=1, k=2 Rule &H36 filtered (after transformation to r=3). NB the scales of (a) and (b) are different.*

44

shows how the world evolves as the interaction rule—the Fundamental Law of Physics, or the Theory of Everything—is applied. What is represented is a history of this particular world (up to an arbitrary point). We might refer to this type of image as a 'bitmap' (BMP) image of this world, as it contains all there is to know about it— the description is *complete*. Whereas a JPEG description would employ an algorithm to compress the image (i.e., extract trends or dominant patterns) via some mathematical shorthand, a BMP image contains complete and perfect information for each and every member of the CA world[12].

There are two important observations to be noted concerning such CA worlds. The first is that almost all initial configurations evolve to configurations with the same statistical properties, i.e., they are qualitatively equivalent (Wolfram, 1985). It is the rule of interaction (the lookup table) that determines the structure that emerges, not the initial conditions. Even if the initial conditions were random, the overall *qualitative* evolution would be unaffected, i.e., the statistical properties of the evolution of these CA worlds is *independent of their starting conditions*[13], i.e., there is no chaos present.

---

12. Note that as a BMP image becomes more complex, or random, the size of the corresponding JPEG file would converge to that of the BMP file, i.e., the image would become incompressible.

13. "It remains conceivable, however, that there exists cellular automata in which two sets of initial states that occur with nonzero probabilities could lead to two qualitatively different forms of behavior" (Wolfram, 1985: 173).

Secondly, and possibly more importantly, despite the elementary underlying mechanics of such systems they "support a whole hierarchy of structures, phenomena, and properties" (Toffoli, 1984: 119). Though it is not obviously apparent from the example given, it is possible to extract some sketchy properties for these emergent 'entities' allowing a rough appreciation of how they might interact. The recognition and ontological status of these emergent entities will be the focus of the middle section of this essay.

Before we move onto exploring alternative representations, or expressions, of the BMP space, there are a couple of additional observations that need to be reported. Quoting Toffoli (1984: 120) again,

...because of the cellular automata's intrinsic discreteness, here numerical integration is an exact process (there are no truncation of round-off error to worry about), and the results that one obtains have thus the force of theorems. In other words, any properties that one discovers through simulation are guaranteed to be properties of the model itself rather than simulation artifact.

We can therefore explore the implications for the philosophy of science in a very rigorous manner. We might refer to this as a *digital philosophy* given the discrete nature of the underlying reality. Through the scientific methods of computational mechanics we can begin to explore fundamental issues concerning the status of human knowledge and the objects to which that knowledge relates. Historically, these ontological and epistemological issues have belonged exclusively to the realms of philosophy rather than science.

Domain Filtering and Computational Mechanics

Wuensche Neighborhood Filtering
Although the existence of some kind of emergent particle dynamics is apparent in Figure 5a, it is not particularly easy to extract with the eye alone. In this section we will briefly consider two ways in which the 'background' might be filtered/removed to reveal an emergent level of dynamics not obviously apparent from the BMP level and certainly not apparent from the elementary rule-based description, i.e., the 'Law of Physics'.

Wuensche (1999), and Wuensche and Lesser (1992) present a very simple way of filtering background patterns to reveal quasi-particle behavior. This particular filtering technique simply considers the most frequently applied rules at each time step and applies a simple algorithm to remove cells that result from the application of these particular rules. In Figure 5b the fourteen most frequently applied neighborhoods (averaged over a window of 10 time steps) are removed to reveal the hidden particle dynamics.

Even though this approach offers a relatively simple method for revealing particle dynamics, Wuensche offers no analysis of the resulting emergent dynamics. For a formal and rigorous analysis of emergent particle dynamics we turn

47

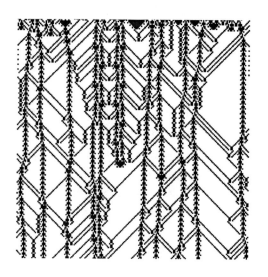

Figure 6 *(a) r=1, k=2, rule 54
(decimal) filtered. Taken from
Hanson (1999).*

to computational mechanics and in particular
the work of Hanson and Crutchfield (1997),
Crutchfield (1997), and Hanson (1999).

*Computational Mechanics and
Domain/Bases Filtering*
"Computational mechanics is a synthesis of
nonlinear dynamics and computation theory,
which characterizes patterns and structure occurring in natural processes by means of formal models of computation... computational
mechanics attempts to discover and characterize the *typical* patterns occurring in a *given*
CA" (Hanson & Crutchfield, 1997: 169-170).
Although computational mechanics is useful in understanding how computations are

48

performed in CAS, we will be more interested in the characterization of the entity dynamics revealed by filtering as an analogy for physical reality.

The first step in distinguishing the 'background' canvas from the 'foreground' particle dynamics is to identity the dominant patterns that define the overall organization of a particular CA[14]. In many CAS, displaying complex dynamics, we find that there are very few important patterns that dominate a system's organization. The set of these dominant patterns is referred to as the system's pattern basis (Hanson & Crutchfield, 1992).

As an example, for the CA system as shown in Figure 5a the dominant pattern is ■ ■ . Once the pattern basis has been identified a mechanical transducer is constructed that parses the space-time data into data that pinpoints domain 'defects' or 'walls', i.e., errors in the pattern basis. Figure 6 shows the result of filtering the 'background' pattern basis for a particular instance of rule 54. By comparing Figure 6 to Figure 5b it is plainly apparent that domain filtering results in a much cleaner impression of the emergent particle dynamics than neighborhood filtering. Hanson and Crutchfield (1997) then go on to identify the four fundamental 'entities' that emerge from the filtering process, and also detail the particle reactions that take place a this level of description (refer to Figure 7b, discussed shortly).

---

14. At the BMP level there is no ontological distinction between the 'foreground' (signal) and the 'background' (noise). The distinction is created through filtering.

111	110	101	100	011	010	001	000
0	0	1	1	0	1	1	0

(a)

$$\alpha + \gamma^- \rightarrow \gamma^- + \alpha + 2\gamma^+$$
$$\gamma^+ + \alpha \rightarrow 2\gamma^- + \alpha + \gamma^+$$
$$\beta + \gamma^- \rightarrow \gamma^+$$
$$\gamma^+ + \beta \rightarrow \gamma^-$$
$$\gamma^+ + \gamma^- \rightarrow \beta$$
$$\gamma^+ + \alpha + \gamma^- \rightarrow \gamma^- + \alpha + \gamma^+$$
$$\gamma^+ + \beta + \gamma^- \rightarrow 0$$

(b)

Figure 7 *(a) The micro-physics of level 0 and (b) the macro-physics of level 1.*

Where the initial transducer uncovered 'defects' in the pattern basis to reveal particles, Hanson and Crutchfield then go on to develop a transducer that uncovers 'defects' at the particle level. This additional step can be used to determine how complete the particle-based (JPEG) description is compared to the CA level (BMP) description as well as uncovering a higher level of entity dynamics. The persistence of defects in the JPEG description indicates that this level of description is incomplete. This shouldn't be a surprise given that this higher level description is a reduction of the BMP level description. However, even though the particle description is incomplete, it is far simpler and more stable for increasing system size.

Hanson and Crutchfield (1997) also present evidence for higher level patterns supporting a hierarchy of interacting entities and entity aggregates.

Referring again to Figure 6, can we infer from this alternative representation of the micro-detailed space-time BMP plot, an alternative representation that is computationally cheaper? The short answer is "yes". For one, we can develop an alternative macro-physics for this apparent dynamical behavior that appears entirely different from the 'micro-physics' of the CA. The alternative macro-physics is shown in Figure 7b, next to the lookup table that represents the micro-physics.

Answering the question of "What is real?" is straightforward enough with the micro-level of cellular automata since only cells (that can be in states '0' or '1') absolutely exist. But can we say with equal confidence that the α-particles referred to in Figure 7b, say, exist in the same sense? Given the filtered version of the space-time diagram showing the apparent evolution of a set of quasi-particles, as well as their compelling macro-physics, it is very tempting indeed to answer in the affirmative. However, it is here that we need to bear in mind how the original patterns are created and how the quasi-particle dynamics is uncovered. The patterns are generated by recursively applying a micro-rule to each cell in the system in order to generate the subsequent system state. Each cell is treated exactly the same as the others—none receive any special or unique treatment. The application of the rule does not change as the system configuration evolves. And, most importantly, each cell in the configuration depends on the states of all the other cells—a particular sequence of 0s and 1s representing the evolution of a particular cell only occurs that way because all the other cells (co)evolve in their particular way. Although the rule is only applied locally, the dynamics that emerge are a result of interactions that extend globally. So α-particles only emerge because β-particles emerge (as well as the other particles)—the emergence of α-particles does not occur independently of the emergence of β-particles—they 'co-emerge'; they depend upon each other for their very existence.

It would be a mistake therefore to assume that the same degree of ontological autonomy can be associated with these particles as with the BMP cellular matrix itself, although, of course, the macro-physical description provides evidence that making the assumption of particle-level autonomy is for many intents and purposes acceptable. However, as with all assumptions, just because making the assumption leads to useful explanations, it does not follow that the assumption is correct. Even the motion of these particles is only apparent, not real—it is simply the result of reapplying the CA rule for each cell at each time step.

We can conclude from these remarks that emergent products, α, β, and γ quasi-particles, primarily exist as such in the alternative macro-level description of the CA. This change in perspective is equivalent to an ontological shift since the existence of the emergent products is a 'feature' of the new perspective. Certainly this new perspective is an incomplete description, yet the fact it is complete with respect to the ascertainment of new laws (axioms) at this higher level would suggest a *substantial realism* on the part of the particles on which the new description is based. For this reason we say that although the particles may not be seen to exist by just considering at the micro-level alone, they do indeed exhibit substantial realism and as such, for certain intents and purposes, can be treated *as if* they were real—for this reason they are referred to as *quasi-particles* rather than the more absolutist term 'particles'. This conclusion concurs with John Holland's architectonic viewpoint on emergence as a descriptive device as long as we extend these speculations to, as Holland (1998) puts it, changes of three orders of magnitude or more. For Holland, macro laws are like additional axioms that enable research to proceed much more easily.

So what is considered real is what still remains after the filtering process is complete. What has been removed consequently is often called background 'noise', when really what we have accomplished is the removal of 'details' not 'noise', for the sake of obtaining a representation with which we can do 'science'.

The emergence of quasi-entities that seem to follow their own set of rules is even more apparent in a particular CA described by the Cambridge mathematician John Conway in 1970, known as the Game of Life (refer to en.wikipedia.org/wiki/Conway's_Game_of_Life for more details).

Conway's Game of Life

As with CA I'm not going to include a full description of the Game of Life. The interested reader is strongly encouraged to refer to William Poundstone's excellent text, *The Recursive Universe* (1985) and to explore Paul Callahan's (2004) interactive website[15] (though other examples are easily found). For the purpos-

---

15. In fact it is very difficult indeed to appreciate the full significance of the Game of Life without interacting with it dynamically, which of course is greatly limited by traditional publishing methods. In Dennett's (1991) opinion, "every philosophy student should be held responsible for an intimate acquaintance with the Game of Life. It should be considered an essential tool in every thought-experimenter's kit, a prodigiously versatile generator of philosophically important examples and thought experiments of admirable clarity and vividness."

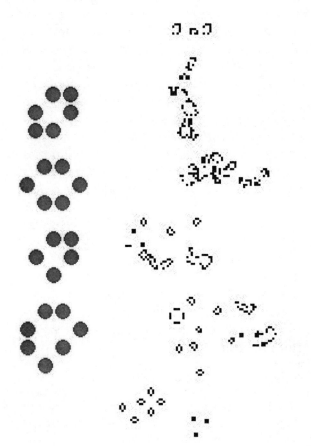

Figure 8 '*Objects' in the Life Universe*

es herein I will simply regurgitate Dennett's (1991: 37) brief introduction to the Game of Life, or *Life*.

Life is played on a two-dimensional grid [as opposed to the 1-d examples already given], *such as a checkerboard or a computer screen; it is not a game one plays to win… The grid divides space into square cells, and each cell is either* ON *or* OFF *at each moment. Each cell has eight neighbors: the four adjacent cells north, south, east, and west, and the four diagonals: northeast, southeast, southwest, and northwest. Time in the Life world is also discrete, not continuous; it advances in ticks, and the state of the world changes between each tick according to the following rule:*

Each cell, in order to determine what to do in the next instant, counts how many of its eight neighbors is ON *at the present instant. If the answer is exactly two, the cell stays in its present state* (ON *or* OFF) *in the next instant. If the answer is exactly three, the cell is* ON *in the next instant whatever its current state. Under all other conditions the cell is* OFF.[16]

---

16. The shorthand way of expressing this rule is 23/3. The '2' and the '3' that appear to the left of the '/' indicate that if exactly two or three neighbors of a particular cell are ON then at the next time step, the state of that particular cell will remain the same regardless of it's previous state. The '3' appearing to the right of the '/' indicates that if exactly three neighbors are ON then the state of the cell in the next time step will be ON regardless of what it was before. For all other combination, i.e. for neighborhoods where 0, 1, 4, 5, 6, 7, and 8 cells are ON, then the cell is turned OFF. In summary, the numbers to the left

The entire physics of Life world is captured in that single unexceptional law.

What one finds in exploring the *Life* world is that some structures (patterns) emerge that seem to be entities unto themselves. Despite *Life* being a simple recursive system, these entities seem to maintain themselves and move around the checkerboard in *quasi*-determinable ways, as well as 'interact' with other entities (see for example Poundstone, 1985, Ch. 2). Figure 8 illustrates this to a very limited degree. Along the top of the figure from left to right are four such entities that have been named 'loaf', 'boat', 'beehive', and 'ship' respectively. There are many others such as 'blinkers', 'period-2 oscillators', 'gliders', etc., some of which are incredibly intricate. The main image in Figure 8 is a snapshot in the history of a *Life* configuration known as 'Puf Train' (Callahan, 2004). Now we can get to the heart of the *Life* matter. Again, in Dennett's (1991: 39) words:

… should we really say that there is real motion in the Life world, or only apparent motion? The flashing pixels on the computer screen are a paradigm case, after all, of what a psychologist would call apparent motion. Are there really gliders that move, or are there just patterns of cell state that move? And if we opt for the latter, should we say at least that these moving patterns are real?

---

refer to 'survival' whereas the numbers of the right refer to 'birth'. This description is equivalent to the one given in the text.

Whichever way one chooses to go with the answer to this question, one must bear in mind that *Life* researchers have discovered rules of interaction for these 'entities' which implies that "their salience as real things is considerable, but not guaranteed" (Dennett, 1991). So even though we can be sure that these 'entities' do not *really* exist, the fact that *they can be treated as* having some level of existence is a staggering discovery as it allows us to work with a higher-level (JPEG), albeit approximate, ontology other than the BMP one. These entities, or parts, can be used to construct a high-level system that would be nigh on impossible to do if we were restricted to the BMP domain. In short, *Life* shows that we can legitimately invoke alternative higher-level quasi-ontologies that are reasonable approximations of the *absolutely correct* BMP ontology, in which only ON/OFF cells exist. Complex systems are therefore tractable, or compressible, to a degree.

Again in Dennett's (1991: 39) words, what is so incredible with *Life* is "that there has been a distinct ontological shift as we move between levels; whereas at the physical [BMP] level there is no motion, and only individuals, cells, are defined by their fixed spatial location, at this design [JPEG] level we have the motion of persisting objects..." This observation will be central when we try to paint a picture of a CA Universe in the next section, and justify the legitimacy of not only science, but other types of knowledge. Before we move on, I will summarize the discussion thus far presented concerning the ontological status of boundaries from a complex systems perspective by simply saying that there exists a continuum of quasi-boundary stabilities which both facilitates and hinders the development of knowledge of any kind. One other point to reiterate is that *Life* is perfectly deterministic—if the game is rerun with the same rules and configuration, *exactly the same history* will be produced—"[e]verything that happens in *Life* is predestined" (Poundstone, 1985: 25). To be exact, what we should say is that *Life* is forward-deterministic but not backward-deterministic as "a [particular] configuration has only one future but (usually) many possible pasts" (Poundstone, 1985: 48).

EXPLORING THE UNIVERSE AS A COMPLEX SYSTEM

T hough the difficulties in fully understanding complex systems are considerable, they are not insurmountable, particularly if one can assume that well-defined isolated complex systems actually do exist and can be easily identified. However, I will argue in this section (following on from the previous argument) that no systems actually exist in a strict sense. This observation may seem to be rather trivial, but the methodological differences that arise if the notion of a complex system is problematized are considerable. In this section I will explore the implications of assuming that there is only one true system and that is the Universe itself—an indivisible whole. Though it is impossible to prove in any scientific sense, I begin by making the assumption that the Universe is a CA experiment, in that it comprises an unimaginably large number of non-linearly interacting elements. Why would we want to consider this to be the case? To realize Laplace's dream of having absolutely Truthful knowledge then, "[t]he state of everything—everywhere —at every time—must be defined. The most economical way to specify such information is through a complexity-generating recursion of physical law" (Poundstone, 1985: 231) like in *Life*. According to the latest physical theories these interacting elements might be incredibly minute superstrings that oscillate in ten-dimensional 'space', where the oscillation frequency of a string corresponds to a particular fundamental particle, such as a top-quark for example (but this needn't be the case at all). This view of the Universe is incredibly simple, yet it has the capacity (because of the recursive application of a simple non-linear rule) to account for everything we observe in our view of reality and a lot more besides. It is the capacity of non-linearity to create an infinitude of different structures (and sub-structures) and behaviors that lead to this possibility. Conway, the inventor of *Life*, "showed that the Life universe ... is not fundamentally less rich than our own" (Poundstone, 1985: 24).

A Cellular Automata Universe and the Status of Scientific Knowledge

Imagine if you will an 11-dimensional (a little hard to imagine I know) CA model comprising a vast number of 'superstring' automatons whose evolution is determined by a single simple rule; the fundamental Law of Physics. Each step in the Universe's evolution is simply the result of this rule being applied to each automaton. This view is impossible to prove of course—like other Theories of Everything (ToEs) endeavors it is more ironic science (Horgan, 1996: 3), or pseudo-science, than science—but its explanatory powers are surprisingly impressive indeed. Though the CA perspective cannot be conclusively proved, an exploration of the consequences that lead from this picture are very revealing. These consequences bring us no closer to a proof of the model, but they do demonstrate the utility of this approach; its capacity

61

to provide a common context for many different discourses is quite impressive indeed.

A Deterministic Universe
The first observation is that such a Universe
would be completely 100 % deterministic:

*... in the Life world ... there is no noise, no uncer-
tainty, no probability less than one. Moreover,
it follows ... that nothing is hidden from view.
There is no backstage; there are no hidden variables...* (Dennett, 1991: 38).

The entire evolution of the Universe would
be totally predetermined by the characteristics of the comprising superstrings and the one
(non-linear) rule of interaction. This would
please our scientific forefathers' view of a Universe as a perfectly tuned machine. For such a
construction it is quite possible that there isn't
even any need for particular initial conditions;
the initial conditions could be completely random and the consequent Universe would still
be the same. (The initial conditions of the Universe have been a hot topic of discussion for
some time. It is only recently that it has been
suggested that maybe there are models of the
Universe that do not require initial conditions
in the traditional sense at all (Chown, 1998;
Tegmark, 1998)—as with the 1-d CA experiments earlier, the initial configuration might
be random with qualitatively the same consequences.) This suggested model of the Universe is based upon a radically realist ontology;
what truly exists are '11-d superstrings' (or,

whatever turns out to be the viable candidate, although scientists may never know), no more, no less. All other 'objects', 'entities', 'boundaries', whatever, are no more than different combinations of 'cell states' that manifest themselves as the 'loaves', 'ships' and 'beehives' of *Life*. In this Universe a fermion is a type of 'boat', say, having no absolute existence, but having a substantial realism, so substantial in fact as to often allow its absolute existence to be taken for granted. An atom is no more than a 'fleet of ships' in this *Life* Universe. Even we humans are not as we appear to ourselves. We are not sentient beings with free will and learning capacities. A human is just a collection of interacting 'boats', 'ships', 'beehives', 'super-beehives', i.e., a very intricate 'cell state' whose occurrence is inevitable in a CA Universe.

A CA Universe would allow other ontologies to be assumed without having to deal directly with the BMP ontology of an unimaginable number of interacting 'superstrings'. It is of the utmost importance to acknowledge that such ontological shifts are imperfect; the complexity of a CA Universe is indeed tractable, but at a cost. But, it is this very ability to profit from alternative quasi-ontologies that enables science to function at all. Without this characteristic mathematics could not exist at all; mathematics deals with 'loaves' and 'ships', not with *Life* 'cell states'. Indeed, it is this very point that even allows the existence of a being capable of making such ontological leaps in the first place.

Another fascinating outcome of assuming a CA Universe is that there is no adaptation in any absolute sense of the term. At the BMP level, the ultimate objective reality, 'superstrings' do not learn new tricks; they do not become 'superduperstrings' (unless it is through an ontological shift on our part). Adaptation is a feature of an ontology that scientists have chosen to take for granted; it is a way of usefully understanding the changes in the *Life* 'cell states' without having to deal *directly* with those *real* 'cell states'. So when complexologists are heard speaking of complex adaptative systems (CASS), they are taking some enormous strides away from what absolutely exists. A great number of assumptions have to be made before one can even infer the (quasi-) existence of CASS. So, even the ontology that complexologists hail as the best lens to view certain 'parts' of the Universe through, are kidding themselves to some extent. Even the CAS ontology is a poor to reasonable JPEG approximation of the absolute BMP reality.

And what of causality? Causation as a necessary connection between two events in a CA Universe cannot be inferred from correlation or association in any *real* sense. Causality, like *Life*'s 'boats' and 'ships' is an emergent 'cell state' pattern that can only be recognized as such by making an ontological shift away from the BMP view that assumes its existence. Causality as experienced by us mere mortals, is an abstraction rather than a *real* operating process. The psychotherapist Carl Jung wrote (with the cooperation of the eminent physicist Wolfgang Pauli) a provocative treatise on this exact point: what "if the connection between cause and effect turns out to be only statistically valid and only relatively true…"? (Jung, 1973: 5). Though as Hume has already noted, "causation is a notion fundamental to human cognition, so fundamental that it is unlikely to ever be eradicated" (Wagner, 1999: 83.), and so it shouldn't. Whether causation is *real* or not, it has proven to be a very productive concept.

A Theistic Observer

In the CA view of the Universe there is no room for free will and choice—that would go against the whole notion of determinism. Consciousness does not exist as such. All decisions, actions, utterances that we each make were all predetermined from the moment of creation (assuming that the idea of a beginning, and therefore time, actually makes any sense in this context)[17]. Even the fact that I am sitting in my home office in Litchfield Park, AZ at 11:53 in the morning, composing this specific paragraph was inevitable (once the initial conditions had been selected[18]). This all sounds a little farfetched, though there are devout religionists who would readily accept it (and since when has 'farfetchedness' been a reliable counter indicator for good theory anyway!). But assuming that the Universe is deterministic,

---

17. The CA description does include a notion of Universal Time, but this would not be experienced by 'beings' existed within such a Universe.

18. Although the qualitative nature of the Universe would be independent of initial conditions, the quantitative detail would be dependent upon the particular initial conditions applied.

who or what would this apparent exquisite determinism be visible to? Cilliers (1998: 4-5) has argued that no thing that exists within a complex system can have complete knowledge of that system. For us, as mere mortals participating within the Universe, we would have to construct a model that represented all 10^{93} (Chown, 2000), or whatever the colossal number is, of superstrings that made up the Universe and step-through the overall evolution. Now, given that we're inside the Universe and only have limited resources available to us from within that same Universe, how could we possibly represent the entire Universe with only a tiny part of the Universe's resources available to us at any one time? Again the simple answer is that we cannot[19].

From this simple argument it is clear that, if the Universe is indeed deterministic, this determinism is (thankfully) beyond us; we will never conceive of an experiment that would otherwise persuade us of our own sentience. The Universe's determinism could only possibly be visible to an external entity; a theistic (meaning 'outside') being. If you like, this is God. However, such a God would have to have sufficient resources available to model the entire created Universe. To It, the determinism of the Universe would be plainly apparent (assuming the Model ran faster than the Universe itself) like the determinism of the CA experi-

---

19. This has been demonstrated in a more sophisticated way in Wolpert (2001), in which it is mathematically demonstrated that it is impossible to process information faster than the Universe can.

ments in previous sections is plainly apparent to the outside human observer. Furthermore, given that a model of more degrees of freedom, i.e., greater complexity, than the Universe itself would have a richer set of behaviors than the Universe, this model would have to be the same as the Universe—the Universe itself is its best model. And, assuming that intractability also restricts a theistic being, then It would have to run It's deterministic universal model before the Universe was created to ensure that it turned out as desired (because there would be no algorithmic shortcut to the future—unless It was happy to rely upon a scrappy JPEG version, which would give unreliable results)[20]. Of course, some would argue that such an entity would not be limited by such fundamental mathematical limitations.

However, we are not totally blind to the Universe's inherent determinism. The fact that 'we' even exist and that 'we' have constructed Laws (from the mathematical representation of 'loaves' and 'boats') that allow us to make quite accurate predictions, accurate enough to build technology for example, shows that we do indeed obtain glimpses of a clockwork Universe.

On the Reasonableness of a Deterministic Universe

Given that some of the remarks above concerning the implications of a deterministic Universe may seem somewhat absurd to some, if not all, readers, I'd like to briefly explore the reasonableness of this proposal.

---

20. Perhaps this Universe is in fact God's trial run!

Presently, in the materialist world of Physics there are two dominant theories of reality: general relativity and quantum mechanics, and one of the most challenging areas of Physics today is the effort to unify these two descriptions. However, there is a problem. General relativity is a deterministic (classical) theory, and quantum mechanics is a probabilistic one, i.e., in the quantum world events do not occur deterministically (with a probability of one), but probabilistically (with a probability of less than one). Does this mean that quantum theory and general relativity are irreconcilable?

Thus far it was believed that the classical [such as general relativity] *and quantum descriptions of nature were so entirely different that one could not be derived from the other* (Morey, 2002: 4).

But,

Contrary to common belief, it is not difficult to construct deterministic models where stochastic behavior is correctly described by quantum mechanical amplitudes... ('t Hooft, 2002: 1).

In the same 2002 article, Nobel Prize winner Gerard 't Hooft, explores the possibility of a deterministic layer existing beneath quantum mechanics, and even suggests that:

Nature's fundamental laws are defined at the Planck scale [herein indirectly referred to as the BMP level]. *At that scale, all we have is* bits of information [or, *Life's* cell states perhaps] (original emphasis, 't Hooft, 2002: 10).

68

The details of 't Hooft's deterministic layer are beyond the scope of our present discussion (and there is a growing literature on this topic available to the interested and mathematically well-versed reader to explore). My reasons for mentioning it at all are to illustrate that a deterministic theory of everything, despite some of its apparently absurd implications (as observed by entities living *within* the Universe), is actually a serious and reasonable possibility in the domain of modern Physics—I would even go to far as to suggest that there is more support in favor of material determinism than the vast majority of the social theories that we tend to accept more readily (perhaps for no other reason than they are often couched in language and concepts more readily understood by the non-Physicist!).

Given that objective reality may well indeed be deterministic, does this raise the possibility of a "classical Physics", say, of the social world? Most certainly not.

[T]*he underlying determinism of nature may be so complex and chaotic that, except in very simple cases, we must resort to a stochastic description for real world calculations* (Morey, 2002: 4).

In other words, if the Universe really is deterministic, direct observation of it is well beyond mortal man.

Now we have considered the strange Universe as observed from the outside-in, we next consider the more accessible view from the inside-out.

Theism versus Atheism

From within the Universe it is impossible to have a perfect representation of anything. There is only one true system; all other systems are temporary and contingent structures whose boundaries are, in a strict sense, illusory. From the view that boundaries are hard resilient structures that demarcate the part from the whole, no boundaries actually exist (except those that define the Universal Cellular Automata). Despite this *no-boundary hypothesis*, which naturally demands an unachievable radically holist approach to knowledge creation if one wants *True* (capital 'T') knowledge, models that do indeed assume boundaries do have considerable practical use.

Although it is interesting that such a complex systems view does lead to differences in knowing dependent upon a theistic (without) and atheistic (within) position, it is not of much help to us as members (however *unreal*) of the Universe. However, it is interesting that such a vision of the Universe provides a common context that allows the Universe to be both deterministic and non-deterministic, depending upon the position of an observer—determinism and probabilism are two sides of the same coin. Such a vision has the capacity to allow for the coexistence of apparently opposing positions. Although it may seem to provide little value when considering the Universe as a whole (afterall, what are the chances of us finding ourselves on the outside looking in?), what if we could approximate parts of the Universe that *appear* to be *real* systems in their own right as complex systems, or even CASS? Again, it is the ability to associate substantial realism to the various *Life* 'entities' that facilitate (or even allow) this activity. Our own existence as such can only be realized by making a shift from *The Universal Ontology* of *Life* to a non-real (albeit substantially real) ontology—human existence is a(n) (quasi-) arbitrary paradigm rather than a given absolute.

The complex systems view differentiates between the knowledge one can obtain when we regard ourselves as outside a (particular) system (of 'loaves'), and that the knowledge we can obtain when regarding ourselves as a member of the system. This view demonstrates that the subject-object distinction often made does limit the knowledge we can have in some way. How much can an outside consultant know about a particular organization, and how valuable is his/her knowledge? What is more important, the opinions of members of society, or the view of politicians often seen as disengaged from society? How much can an earthbound science know about the Universe *in which* it is supported? We will not investigate this aspect of complexity much further but, it is interesting to note that complexity thinking does legitimize both (inter) subjective knowledge as well as objective knowledge, albeit in an imperfect way[21]. We need to ask ourselves: if science claims to extract *real* patterns (which from the

---

21. In fact, it suggests that objective knowledge is really just very stable subjective knowledge. We might also say that subjective knowledge is really objective knowledge within a narrowly defined context.

discussion on *Life* has shown not to be the case —science considers 'loaves' and 'blinkers' that do not *ultimately exist*) to what extent are those patterns more *real* than the patterns we each extract from our surroundings in the process of sense-making. Are our personal opinions based upon patterns *less real* than those found in science? Why should science be allowed to claim that the 'objects' it considers are more real than the 'objects' we each 'see' in our daily lives? In what sense are the boundaries of an 'electron' more real than my own personal boundary that defines 'friend' given that neither is *absolutely real*? (Often, the ability to make accurate predictions is the only differentiating factor, which is quite unreasonable given the different nature of these 'entities'.)

Boundary (or, Pattern) Distributions

The fundamental conclusion that the complexity-based argument given thus far leads to is that there are no boundaries in the Universe except those that define its fundamental components (superstrings?). How are we to do derive knowledge of particular systems then (particularly if no systems *really* exist)? As mentioned above the situation is not as dire as it might immediately seem. There is no need to follow the radical holists to model the world, the Universe and everything (which we could not do even if we wanted to). As the argument above suggests, there is strong evidence that, although there may be no boundaries, there are resilient and relatively stable emergent structures, or patterns, that can be treated with a *reason-*

able degree of accuracy as *having existence.* In fact, there is a distribution of boundary, or entity, stabilities. No evidence is given herein for what this distribution may actually be; it is simply argued that there is a distribution. Figure 9 illustrates a possible stability distribution (which has no firm theoretical or empirical basis—with all the interest in self-organized criticality maybe a power-law curve would be more appropriate).

At one end of the stability spectrum there are boundaries/structures that are so persistent and stable that, for most intents and purposes, it can safely be assumed that they are in fact real and absolute. Boundaries that describe the objects of science-based technology exist toward this end of the spectrum. Such long-term stability allows a 'community of enquirers', e.g., the scientific community, to inter-subjectively converge on some agreed principles that might actually be tested through experiment. Under such conditions it is quite possible to develop quasi-objective knowledge, which for most intents and purposes (but *not ultimately*) is absolute. The existence of such persistent boundaries, or patterns, allows for something other than a radically holistic analysis—this accounts for why the scientific program has been in many ways so successful when it comes to technological matters—it has hit upon a very powerful quasi-ontology. In many circumstances reductionism (the assumption that 'beehives' actually do *exist*) is a perfectly valid, although still approximate, route to understanding. In short, what is suggested here is that scientific

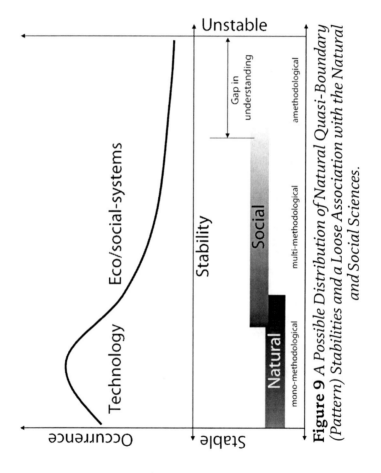

Figure 9 *A Possible Distribution of Natural Quasi-Boundary (Pattern) Stabilities and a Loose Association with the Natural and Social Sciences.*

study depends upon the assumption that natural boundaries are static in a sense, and that if one can 'prove' that the boundaries of interest are in fact stable and persistent, then traditional reductionist scientific methods are more than up to the task of generating actionable knowledge.

It is exactly this stability, this apparent 'movement' of persistently stable 'entities' (as is observed in *Life*), that can be attributed some substantial level of realism, that allows us as modeller's/scientists/observers to "proceed to predict—sketchily and riskily—the behavior of larger configurations or systems of configurations, without bothering to compute the physical [BMP] level" (Dennett, 1991: 40); an enormous computational saving indeed. It is exactly this *substantial realism of levels* (or quasi-entities) that supports the efficacy of the hierarchy of sciences without having to know everything there is to know about each ascending level away from the fundamental physical 'superstring' reality.

At the other end of the stability spectrum we have essentially 'noise', in which the lifetime of apparent boundaries might be so fleeting as to render them unrecognizable as such and therefore essentially unanalyzable. Under such circumstances attempts to develop 'knowledge' (it is not clear to me that this is even a reasonable concept at this end of the spectrum) are strongly determined by the whims of the individual, with observed boundaries being more a function of our thirst to make sense, rather than an actual feature of 'reality'. To maintain a purely positivistic position, one would have to accept radical holism and consider the entire Universe—a practical absurdity and a theoretical impossibility, as has already been stated. This is the only method by which truly robust knowledge could possibly be derived.

Fortunately, the vast majority of the perceived Universe isn't quite so nebulous. This doesn't mean, however, that boundary recognition and allocation is a trivial exercise. In fact without the ability to not only determine the stability distribution, but also recognize where the objects of interest might exist on the *continuum of stabilities*, it is very difficult to determine how to approach them. Radical positivists might argue that a rigorous implementation of reductionist scientific methods are appropriate across the board. I have already suggested that the application of such methods makes clear assumptions about the ontological status of boundaries that I believe cannot be supported. This position sympathizes with Shweder's (2001) argument that, as science was designed to study observable material entities that can easily be located in time and space, there are subjects beyond the proper realm of science. Relating this back to *Life*: the ontological leap from the physical (BMP) reality to the 'design [JPEG] level' (Dennett, 1991) of 'loaves', 'boats', 'ships', etc., is imperfect, therefore some, what is generally referred to as 'noise', is removed to allow the leap to occur. Science does not, and cannot, deal with (all) the 'noise'. Arguably, the social sciences, with their willingness to work with a plurality of (possibly incommensurable)

76

methods and perspectives, to view the patterns from different angles and therefore at different 'noise' levels, is more suited to deal with a state of affairs in which both boundary recognition and allocation are deeply problematic. This position reflects Cilliers's (2001: 142) concern that "[i]n accepting the complexity of the boundaries of complex systems, we are committed to be critical about how we use the notion since it affects our understanding of such systems, and influences the way in which we deal with them."

ToEs

Laughlin & Pines (2000: 28) define a ToE as: "the ultimate theory of the Universe—a set of equations capable of describing all phenomena that have been observed, or that will ever be observed." It is clear from the CA description of the Universe from within that I do certainly support the view that there may indeed exist some ultimate realist theory of everything (although the details are elusive, the qualitative nature of it are provided herein, i.e., the ToE will be a representation of an ensemble of automata of dimension n—which is currently speculated to be about 10 or 11—governed by one simple non-linear interactive rule). However, given the difficulties in making accurate abstractions from limited evidence, as discussed earlier it is impossible for us to ever know if our proposed ToE is *the* ToE as there are many ways to draw the same conclusions[22]. Furthermore, *even if*

---

22. The technical term for this in systems theory is *equi-*

we could obtain sufficient evidence to demonstrate that we have the ultimate ToE, its value would be questionable. Bootstrapping from one level to another is hard enough in simpler cellular-automata-like models (though *Life* shows that it can be done in a crude manner) let alone CA models that contain a universal number of non-linearly interacting superstrings. So, a ToE does exist (perhaps!), but its use would be incredibly limited, unless of course we somehow overcome the fundamental limitations of computational intractability (as well as not having access to the entire Universe's resources!). That scientists might bootstrap from superstrings to cells or social systems is nothing more than a dream.

So what options are we left with? A biological description of humans, for example, is incomplete because it makes assumptions about the efficacy of particular cellular, or multi-cellular, boundaries that are not completely real. At least with Biology, the subject matter presents itself in a manner that justifies the isolated study of well-defined objects. What if we considered a social system? What boundaries would we infer? How might we define the system? What language (which itself depends upon boundary allocations) would we use? The first step in dealing with this 'grey' state of affairs is to acknowledge the metaphorical nature of all representation systems, including mathematics.

---

finality (Bertalanffy, 1998: 40).

Theory as Metaphor

Given that there are no *True* boundaries, we are forced to assume at least some boundaries because of our access to limited resources. Some of these boundary judgments will be reasonable (the possibility to leap fruitfully from the physical level of *Life* 'cell states' to the design level of 'ships' demonstrates this), some of them will not be (because of 'noise'). Given that there can be no *complete* description, it is easy to conclude that all descriptions must necessarily be metaphorical in nature. Even mathematical models are metaphors for reality.

A metaphor is a partial description of one thing in terms of another. In the case of mathematics, the Universe (one thing) is partially described in terms of selected mathematical constructs (i.e., other things). As all explanations must be, by their very nature, metaphorical then we must treat them as such rather than implicitly assuming that our explanations are isomorphic with the objects they claim to describe. This is not as big a disaster for our scientific knowledge as it might first sound. Although we will never (knowingly) obtain the Truth, all our words, concepts and theories can point toward the Truth without ever fully expressing it. Our supposed Truths still make 'useful fictions,' or as Stewart & Cohen (1997: 37) refer to them, 'lies-to-children.' As the eminent French physicist Louis de Broglie once said: "May it not be universally true that the concepts produced by the human mind, when formulated in a slightly vague form, are roughly valid for reality, but that, when extreme

79

precision is aimed at, they become ideal forms whose real content tends to vanish away?"[23].

To suggest that science, particularly physics, is metaphorical in nature would be verging on blasphemous to some scientists who wish to distinguish their efforts from the 'soft' ways of social science, or the humanities. Maybe this is because "[m]etaphors are often construed to be 'as-if' devices and hence to have no place in a proper scientific description of the world which *pretends* to tell things as they are"[24] (Bradie, 1999: 160). I personally know a number of natural scientists that would be deeply offended at the accusation that science is no more than metaphor. But they need not be so defensive. Science is obviously one of the most successful metaphors ever constructed. Not all metaphors are created equal! However offensive the term metaphor might be to some, its importance lies in the explicit recognition of science's weaknesses as much as its strengths. "Ordinarily, a metaphor suggests an analogy or likeness between two different things by applying the term for one to the other" (Jones, 1982: 3). This is exactly what happens when the leap from 'cell states' to 'ships' is made. As Colin Turbayne points out, "the use of metaphor involves both the awareness of duality of sense and the pretense that the two different senses are one" (quoted in Jones, 1982: 3-4). I assert that the realist position developed herein justifies the view that *all* theory is meta-

---

23. Quoted in Cory, 1942: 268.
24. Italics added.

phor[25]. The problem is that "when metaphors become crystallized and abstract, cut off from their roots in consciousness, and forgotten by their creators, they become idols" (p. 5)[26]. So in pushing this point, I am also trying to warn against the idolatry of science; "[i]t is here that the risk may occur that … [a particular] model becomes the sole object of the scholar's preoccupations" (Constandache, 2000: 1070).

Science, however successful, is built upon an ontological shift away from the absolute reality of *Life*'s 'cell states', and is therefore inherently imperfect and limited in scope. On the other hand I do not accept Jones's (1982) position "that the predictive power of physics was built in and guaranteed from the beginning" and that "[t]hrough a selective creation of quantities and laws, a self-contained system was constructed which gives answers on its own terms and arbitrarily rules out what it cannot deal with as nonquantative or nonphysical" (p. 44). To my mind, science is more than a self-fulfilling prophecy—the existence of science, is an inevitable result of a CA Universe that contains 'objects' whose substantial realism allows for science to make such claims of objectivity. The idolatry of science is simply an unfortunate by-product of its own success, and scientists'

---

25. The conclusion that all theory is metaphor will be of no surprise to postmodernist thinkers, though it may be a surprise to them that the conclusion can be 'derived' from a radically realist foundation.

26. For more on the nature of metaphor and the role it plays in the sense making process refer, as examples, to Lakoff & Johnson (1980), and Allbritton (1995).

general failure (consciously or not) to communicate their favored topic's shortcomings to the wider 'user' community.

Now that a complexity-based picture of the Universe has been painted and explored, I would now like to turn toward a possible philosophical solution to the problems that such a portrait conveys. Again, the argument to come hinges on the ability to make ontological shifts, however "sketchily and riskily," away from the truly physical world of *Life* 'cell states', as well as our answer to the question of how *substantially real* an 'object' or 'pattern' has to be before we can safely *assume* its existence.

TOWARDS AN EVOLUTIONARY PHILOSOPHY

The first step in making an argument for an evolutionary philosophy is to justify ontological (or metaphysical) pluralism. In a way, this step has already been taken (in an incomplete way—theoretically at least) by the observation that a leap from the physical ontology of *Life*'s 'cell states' to a design ontology in which the apparent 'objects' of the physical ontology are treated *as such*, i.e., rather than regarding them as useful 'non-real' approximations, they are accepted as having *substantial realism* that often masquerades as full-blown realism. The hierarchy of the sciences exploits this feature of *Life*'s 'cell states', creating a hierarchy of 'entities' from superstrings to galactic clusters. Each science is reasonably justified with the assumption that its objects of study are *real*. The complex systems view doesn't quite support this linear view. It suggests that each subsequent layer of the hierarchy of entities is an emergent property of the layer below. So, rather than seeing cells (as in biology) as *real*, they are regarded as the emergent products of the molecular (as in chemistry) layer. The problems of bootstrapping from one layer to another have already been discussed (the intractability of the emergent process basically prevents this from ever happening), and even though each of the distinct branches of science probably accept that its particular objects of interest are not *real* in an absolute sense, the assumption that these objects have substantial realism is sufficient to not undermine their efforts much at all (although at the same time such assumptions limits as much as support such efforts). The fact that each science has indeed made great contributions to human understanding is a testament to the accuracy of these various ontological assumptions for certain purposes. In the absence of a bootstrapping method from the physical BMP model, quasi-'ontological pluralism' has been hugely successful. It is quite astounding that science has progressed so far based on poor to good ontological assumptions, but this realization could only be achieved if the Universe was indeed quite stable (in many respects), and again is testament to the power of the ontological shift discussed earlier.

In summary, even though there is a strong argument that suggests that there is only one absolutely *real* level of existence (the BMP level), we are forced on practical grounds (and justified on theoretical grounds) to at least adopt a scientific pluralism that works rather well indeed. Above I refer to this as quasi-'ontological pluralism', in recognition that each of the scientific ontologies are only approximate ontologies, and also that there are only a limited number of these approximate ontologies in science meaning that it is not totally pluralistic. Maybe I should simply say that, according to science, there 'exist' a limited number of *substantially real levels*.

Horizontal and Vertical Pluralism

Even though the above view has the capacity to allow the exploration of the same phenomena from different ontologies, all the ontologies are scientific in nature. This view is exemplified by W. V. Quine's brand of ontological relativism. "Here the plurality consists in the possible existence of a range of alternative scientific worldviews, each empirically adequate to more or less the same degree, and none, even in principle, have privileged claim to provide a 'truer' description of the world" (Price, 1992: 389). Even "incompatible theories can explain the same facts equally well and make equally good predictions" (Masani, 2001: 279). Price (1992: 389) goes on to argue that,

[t]here may be equally valid possible scientific worldviews, but all of them are scientific worldviews, and in that sense are on the same level of linguistic activity. In other words, this is what might appropriately be called horizontal pluralism.

But why should pluralism be restricted to the *horizontal*? Why should pluralism be associated only with what we might call 'discourse monism'? The answers to these questions again depend on how *substantially real* an entity must be for it to be (temporarily) assumed to be *real* (remembering that it has already been argued that no scientific worldview is based on an absolutely True ontology). Scientists would undoubtedly argue that the patterns they develop Natural Laws for, as part of their ongoing investigations, are more real than the patterns that society, or even individuals, deem real. Given the (stable-ish) objects of scientific investigation, then I would generally support this assertion. However, like some social scientists I also believe that the subject matter of the social sciences, as an example, puts them outside the proper realm of science (see Shweder, 2001). The CA view of the Universe also supports this position. Note that this belief *certainly does not* deny the possibility that more traditional scientific approaches have a lot to offer the social sciences (and vice versa). Science is quite intolerant to 'noise'. Scientific methods generally seek to extract clear patterns from the 'noise' of reality. Sometimes this process is straightforward, sometimes it isn't. My point is simply that the pattern extraction process is problematic depending upon the relationship between an observer and the 'noise' of reality. Substantially "real but (potentially) noisy patterns abound in ... the *Life* world, there for the picking up if only we are lucky or clever enough to hit on the right perspective" (Dennett, 1991: 41). Traditional science has a knack of extracting the more apparent patterns and expressing their form in an implementable way (generally through mathematics). What about everything else? Returning to Price (1992: 390):

If these [scientific discourses] *are cases of horizontal pluralism, what would be a vertical pluralism? It would be the view that philosophy should recognise an irreducible plurality of kinds of discourse—the moral as well as the scientific, for example. This is the species of pluralism with which we … [should] be most concerned.*

Price refers to this type of vertical pluralism as *discourse pluralism*. Here we have arrived at a description of what is meant by pluralism in a complexity-informed evolutionary philosophy. This type of pluralism is not *irrealist* at all. It simply accepts that in the absence of a completely realist position, we may profit from the examination of a variety of other worldviews and discourses whose *scales of compression* varies. Different scientific worldviews may be as useful as different moral worldviews or different artistic worldviews (such as cubism or abstract expressionism), all of which are metaphors, or caricatures, of reality. This does not lead to an 'anything goes' postmodernism, except as a starting point. But how, if we are to make a decision one way or another, are we to untangle the pluralist web and agree upon, albeit temporarily and locally, a dominant worldview?

Critical Dialogue as Conceptual Investigation

It would be convenient to address the question above by simply offering a systematic framework that we could employ that would associate each discourse and comprising worldview with a context in which we could be confident that we had selected the best position to base our decisions upon. The problem with any such solution becomes idolatry or reification, so I will not attempt to provide a coherent framework except as to suggest that there are an enormous number of ways to exploit pluralism, each with their own idiosyncrasies. (It is really quite remarkable that these frameworks and methodologies have been largely ignored by the complexity community: see for example Jackson & Key, 1984; Flood, 1995; or Midgley, 2000. Complexity thinking and soft systems thinking share a great deal in common.)

Here I simply argue that it is through critical dialogue that we may temporarily reshape the default position of pluralism to a local monism, i.e., it is through critical dialogue that the *general* is tailored to the *perceived* specific. Critical dialogue here is regarded in much the same way that Socrates and Plato regarded criticism, i.e., "no more baffling an enterprise than investigating a concept" (Gottlieb, 2000: 174). The process is one of an ongoing three-way dialogue between a decision-making body (which may be the one or the many), the *perceived* context (which will undoubtedly evolve and has an obvious role for 'reality'), and the pluralist realm of ideas and theories. The relationship between these three elements is certainly non-trivial and would require extensive investigation to understand fully. But the essence of this process is that the default position is 'nothingness' and that through a critical process 'something' is negotiated that will inform our actions; it is a group decision process (on which there is a wealth of literature already in existence, see for example, Vennix, 1996 and selected chapters in Mingers & Gill, 1997 on multi-methodology). The process is imperfect and explicitly acknowledges the potential of all perspectives—it does not privilege a scientific theory over and above a personal opinion—and is ultimately determined on a changing practical, rather than rigid ideological, basis. As Dennett (1991: 49) writes, "[t]he choice of pattern would indeed be up to the observer, a matter to be decided on idiosyncratic pragmatic grounds." I have referred to this evolutionary philosophy elsewhere (Richardson, 2001, 2004a) as quasi-'critical pluralism' (Q-CP). The 'quasi' is included to explicitly acknowledge the impossibility of being critical-without-bias or truly pluralistic.

This view denies the sort of (naïve) realism that perfectly maps our conceptual boundaries (that are implied by our explanations) to *real* objects (despite being 'constructed' from a purely realist ontology). There is no one-to-one mapping of our ideas, scientific or otherwise, to objective reality. However, this denial of realism (as a default position) does not *recoil* into an argument for constructivism. Constructivists, as I have already said, argue that all boundaries are created in our minds and as such do not correlate with objective reality at all. Q-CP is based upon the distribution of natural boundary/ pattern stabilities (derived from a purely physical foundation) and falls between these two extremes. Rather than having a fixed relationship with natural (quasi) boundaries, or having no relationship at all, our conceptual boundaries do have a complex (surprise, surprise!) and changing relationship with reality. Sometimes this link might be so tenuous as to be unusable. Sometimes this link is so strong as to give us the impression that we might actually have absolute Truth to hand. The key difference between this position and (naïve) realism is that it explicitly acknowledges the problematization of boundary recognition, which is trivialized in many realist philosophies. The key difference between Q-CP and constructivism is that Q-CP acknowledges that the world of *substantially real patterns* does play an integral part in the evolutionary relationship between reality 'out there' and our ideas. Figure 10 attempts to illustrate the changing relationship(s) between our conceptual boundaries and natural boundaries for these different philosophies.

Before offering some final remarks and conclusions I feel the need to provide another justification for why Q-CP does not collapse into a local anything goes relativism, i.e., why it is that some patterns are more real than others, and why simply extracting patterns is in itself not sufficient to claim one has some 'knowledge'.

Intrinsic Emergence

The notion of *intrinsic emergence*, introduced by Crutchfield (1994), offers a computational-based explanation as to why some theories / perspectives / abstractions / etc. are better (at the global level) than others and why we should resist a *local* "anything goes" relativism. According to Crutchfield (1994), "The problem is that the 'newness' in the emergence of pattern is always referred outside the system to some observer that anticipates the struc-

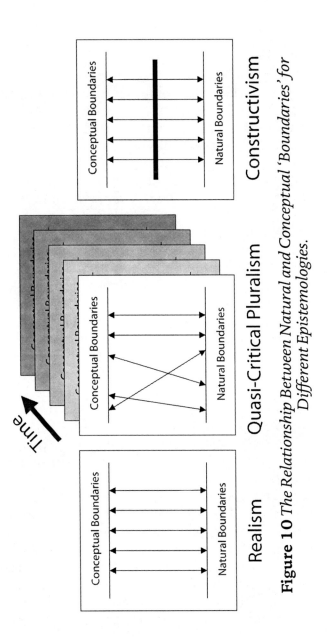

Figure 10 *The Relationship Between Natural and Conceptual 'Boundaries' for Different Epistemologies.*

91

ture via a fixed palette of possible regularities."
This can lead to the relativistic situation mentioned above. Although there is clearly a relativistic dimension to pattern recognition (and therefore theory development) how might we resist a radical relativism that would suggest that anything goes in any context all the time? Crutchfield (1994) goes on to say:

What is distinctive about intrinsic emergence is that the patterns formed confer additional functionality which supports global information processing... [T]he hypothesis ... is that during intrinsic emergence there is an increase in intrinsic computational capability, which can be capitalized on and so can lend additional functionality.

Another way of saying this is that if we, for arguments sake, privilege a computational view of the Universe, the structures that emerge support information processing in some way—they affect the computing ability of the Universe. This would suggest that 'real' patterns are those patterns which can be linked to some Universal computational task. For example, reconsidering Figure 6, if a filter had been chosen that was not based upon the observed pattern basis then a 'pattern' would still have been uncovered, but it is unlikely that, that pattern would have any relevance to the computational capacity of the system—the odds are the pattern would also appear quite disordered and lead to an unnecessarily more complicated macrophysics. This of course opens up the possibility that the best 'filters' are those that extract regular patterns, but given that assessments of regularity (or disorder) lie on a spectrum how do we decide which patterns are sufficiently regular to allow us to associate with them some *functional* importance (and therefore *substantial realism*)? Even though certain patterns play a functional role within the Universe (which suggests in absolute terms that not all patterns are 'real'), it does not follow that we, as participants in the Universe, can unambiguously determine which patterns are significant and which are not. It is not even clear if an 'outsider' could achieve such absolute clarity either.

The notion of intrinsic emergence shows that the patterns that we might consider 'real' allow the system of interest to process information in some way, suggesting that certain patterns are internally meaningful and not arbitrary. It does not follow that just because some patterns are indeed more 'real' than others we can easily determine which are which. In a universal and absolute sense, not all filters and patterns are made equal, and certain filters (and their resultant extracted patterns) are more (functionally) meaningful than others.

This computational perspective simply suggests that the emergence of structure supports efficient computation—so, in a sense, my very existence contributes to Universal Computational Efficency (unless of course the pattern referred to as Kurt Richardson, is nothing more than a curious fluke that has no functional importance whatsoever!). The notion that my very being can be accounted for as a computational convenience is an odd one, to say the least, but the point of introducing the idea is to illustrate that in a CA based view of the Universe, in which pattern detection is intimately tied to knowledge generation, a *localized* anything goes relativism is not justified on rational grounds. Our severely limited ability to pin down the best (i.e., most functionally relevant) representation(s) of a particular (local) aspect of reality encourages both criticism and pluralism. These epistemological strategies come with the understanding that not all patterns are equally adept at explaining the 'data', and that, at least in principle, if not in practice, there does indeed exist a 'best' perspective. In short, intrinsic emergence justifies a *global* position of "anything goes" relativism, whilst at the same time denying a *local* position of "anything goes" relativism, i.e., it limits the jurisdiction of such relativism.

SUMMARY AND CONCLUSIONS

"Controversy always pounces upon the least defensible points in any position which has been advanced. We might well say that, in doing so, controversy follows a law of 'least energy' analogous to the well-known law of dynamics" (Sellars, 1927: 238). An example of this might be how opponents to strong realism, because of its socio-psychological naivety, *recoil* to a social constructivist position. This phenomena is observed all too often in scientific as well as philosophical debate (and especially political and public debate!), i.e., an argument is found lacking in some way, the focus of debate then shifts onto the lacking aspect, which is then generally used to destroy the entire original argument. A new and often totally opposing argument is then proposed that pretends to address the shortcomings of the original argument. I am frequently infuriated with such unsophisticated linear argumentation. The approach implies that there is always a better way and therefore a best way, and that the speaker has some privileged access to it. Rather than seeing all positions as inherently wrong in an *absolute* sense and then seeking to synthesize a view through critical dialogue that attempts to take the 'best of many worlds', we often find ourselves banging our heads against a brick wall of intellectual arrogance and boorishness. In this essay I have attempted to show that even a radically realist (scientific) view of the Universe leads quite naturally to a position that frowns upon any attempts to enforce any sort of intellectual imperialism.

I have argued for the adoption of an evolutionary philosophy/perspective based upon the assumption that the Universe might be well-described *at some arbitrarily deep level* as a CA. Though the argument is indeed based upon a strongly realist ontology it concludes that quasi-ontological pluralism must be admitted, and that it is through critical dialogue that the pros and cons of different ontologies can be determined temporarily and locally. The argument given defends a limited scientific imperialism, and also attempts to make explicit science's inherent limitations, thereby forcing us to consider the possibility of other types of knowledge being equally legitimate *as a starting point.*

In this view the many emerging tools of complexity science are no more than additions to a growing arsenal of tools that facilitate sense-making—they perform better in some contexts and worse in others (and often we cannot tell in advance which). However, where the tools and ideas of complexity science differ is that they inform a perspective that highlights their limitations, and encourages us to approach the real world with an open mind, and to develop our critical and pluralistic skills, i.e., complexity *science* informs a much broader concept of complexity *thinking.* In this essay such complexity thinking has been associated with an evolutionary philosophy labeled (quasi-) critical pluralism, which attempts to level the playing field for all methods and modes for developing understanding so that context relevant understanding is developed, and the bias introduced by one's approaches is overtly explored. The basis of this development is the recognition that the acceptance of the complexity of reality leads quite naturally to the problematization of the existence of boundaries.

It is perhaps interesting to note that despite its realist beginnings, the argument does conclude, in a sense, that anti-realism becomes the natural, initial position in any debate. Even "local triumph's may be insufficient to provide any ground in reality for declaring one account a closer approximation of the truth" (Dennett, 1991: 48). However, even though the default 'universal' position may be anti-realist in this sense, it may manifest itself in an infinitude of ways, including a return to the purely realist position if only temporarily.

One might argue that by privileging ontological and methodological pluralism and critical dialogue I am guilty of the same intellectual imperialism that I am myself critical of. To this I have no real defense, except to say that the resulting philosophy is quite empty in that no systematic framework is offered that will plug the gaps in our knowledge that result from a complex Universe. In a way, I regard the argument herein as no more than a ladder that allows one to climb to a position of philosophical emptiness that highlights the uncertainty of all things and the dangers of idolatry and reification. Once this position is reached, the ladder is thrown away and we get on with our lives. The difference being that, once 'enlightened', all our decisions and attitudes regarding what we think we know are continually treated with a healthy scepticism. We must reify boundaries to interact with the world, but we need to be fully aware that what we reify is often arbitrary, and that reification is a prerequisite to our interaction with the world. Once in this position, all the tools available to us in our attempts to make sense, which includes both those tools commonly associated with complexity science[27], and those that are not (remembering that any and all approaches are legitimate *by default*), can be selectively employed in a critical fashion.

The basis of my argument is that we can have good knowledge of the Universe without necessarily being restricted to considering only what is *absolutely real*. *Life* shows us that we can profit considerably from an ontological shift away from the ultimate reality of *Life*'s 'cell states'. The scale of compression when one moves from the physical (BMP) level to the design (JPEG) level is stupendous, although the knowledge acquired through such a move is at best sketchy and rough. Consider the calculations involved in a game of chess: "it is the difference between figuring out in your head what white's most likely (best) move is versus calculating the state of a few trillion pixels through a few thousand generations" (Dennett, 1991: 42). But deciding what is *substantially real* enough to base our understanding on is inherently problematic and may take many differ-

---

27. Refer to Reschke (2001) for a brief review of the tools commonly associated with complexity science.

ent routes. As far as we should be concerned *nothing is absolutely real* and at the heart of all our philosophies, attitudes, opinions, etc. is a judgment as to what is *substantially real*. The distinction between what is *real* and what is *substantially real* is a subtle one, but it is such subtleties that differentiate between Capitalists, Scientists, Marxists, Theologists (and the other '-ists betwixt and between), as well as what makes each of us intellectually unique. These postmodern-esque conclusions are not new. The fact that they can be derived from a strongly realist approach, however, may surprise some.

ACKNOWLEDGEMENTS

Thanks also go to Caroline, Alexander, Albert and William Richardson for 'weird' diversions. This short book is a much-extended version of Richardson, 2004b.

REFERENCES

Allbritton, D.W. (1995). "When metaphors function as schemas: Some cognitive effects of conceptual metaphors," *Metaphor and Symbolic Activity*, 10(1): 33-46.

Allen, P.M. (2001). "Economics and the science of evolutionary complex systems," *SysteMexico*, 1(2): 29-71.

Backlund A. (2000). "The definition of *system*," *Kybernetes*, 29(4): 444-451.

Bertalanffy, L. v. (1998). *General System Theory: Foundations, Development, Application*, ISBN 0807604534.

Boulding, K. E. (1956). "General systems theory: The skeleton of science," *Management Science*, 2: 197-208.

Bradie, M. (1999). "Science and metaphor," *Biology and Philosophy*, 14: 159-166.

Callahan, P. (accessed 2004), *Wonder's of Maths: Conway's Game of Life*, http://www.math.com/students/wonders/life/life.html.

Chaitin, G. (1975). "Randomness and mathematical proof," *Scientific American*, CCXXXII: 47-52.

Chown, M. (1998), "Anything goes," *New Scientist magazine*, 158(2137): 26.

Chown, M. (2000), "Before the Big Bang," *New*

Scientist magazine, 166(2241): 24.

Cilliers, P. (1998). *Complexity and Postmodernism—Understanding Complex Systems*, ISBN 0415152879.

Cilliers, P. (2001). "Boundaries, hierarchies and networks in complex systems," *International Journal of Innovation Management*, 5(2): 135-147.

Constandache, G.G. (2000). "Models of reality and reality of models," *Kybernetes*, 29(9/10): 1069-1077.

Cory, D. (1942). "The transition from naïve to critical realism," *The Journal of Philosophy*, 39(10): 261-268.

Crutchfield, J.P. (1994). "Is anything ever new? Considering emergence," in G.A. Cowan, D. Pines, and D. Meltzer (eds.), *Complexity: Metaphors, Models, and Reality*, ISBN 9780738202327 (1999), pp. 515-537.

Crutchfield, J.P. (1997). "The calculi of emergence: Computation, dynamics and induction," *Physica D*, 75: 11-54.

Dennett, D.C. (1991). "Real patterns," *The Journal of Philosophy*, 88(1): 27-51.

Edmunds, B. (2000). "Complexity and scientific modelling," *Foundations of Science*, 5: 379-390.

Emmeche, C., Köppe, S. and Stjernfelt, F. (2000). "Levels, emergence, and three versions of downward causation," in *Downward Causation*, P.B. Andersen, C. Emmeche, N.O. Finnemann, and P.V. Christiansen (eds.), ISBN 8772888148.

Fetzer, J.H. and Almeder, R.F. (1993). *Glossary of Epistemology/Philosophy of Science*,

ISBN 1557785589.

Flood, R.L. (1995). "Total systems intervention (TSI): A reconstitution," *Journal of the Operational Research Society*, 46: 174-191.

Gottlieb, A. (2000). *The Dream of Reason: A History of Western Philosophy from the Greeks to the Renaissance*, ISBN 0393049515.

Hanson, J.E. (1999). *The Computational Mechanics of Cellular Automata*, Revised and updated PhD thesis.

Hanson, J.E. and Crutchfield, J.P. (1992). "The attractor-basin portrait of a cellular automaton," *J. Stat. Phys.*, 66: 1415-1462.

Hanson, J.E. and Crutchfield, J.P. (1997). "Computational mechanics of cellular automata: An example," *Physica D*, 103(1-4): 169-189.

Hofstadter, D. (1979). *Gödel, Escher, Bach: An Eternal Golden Braid*, ISBN 046502850.

Holland, J. (1998). *Emergence: From Chaos to Order*, ISBN 9780738201429 (1999).

Horgan, J. (1996). *The End of Science—Facing the Limits of Knowledge in the Twilight of the Scientific Age*, ISBN 0316640522.

Jackson, M. C. and Keys, P. (1984). "Towards a system of systems methodologies," *Journal of Operational Research Society*, 35: 473-486.

Jones, R.S. (1982). *Physics as Metaphor*, ISBN 0816610762.

Jung, C.G. (1973). *Synchronicity: An Acausal Connecting Principle*, ISBN 0691017948.

Kan, I. (1994). "Open sets of diffeomorphisms having two attractors, each with an everywhere dense basin," *Bulletin of the Ameri-*

can Mathematical Society, 31(1): 68-74.

Lakoff, G. and Johnson, M. (1980). *Metaphors We Live By*, ISBN 0226468011.

Langefors, B. (1995). *Essays in Infology*, Studentlitteratur, Lund.

Laughlin, R.B. and Pines, D. (2000). "The theory of everything," *Proceedings of the National Academy of Sciences of the United States of America*, 97(1): 28-31. Available electronically from http://www.pnas.org/cgi/reprint/97/1/28.pdf.

Masani, P. R. (2001). "Three modern enemies of science: Materialism, existentialism, constructivism," *Kybernetes*, 30(3): 278-294.

Midgley, G. (2000). *Systemic Intervention: Philosophy, Methodology, and Practice*, ISBN 0306464888.

Mingers, J. and Gill, A. (1997). *Multimethodology: The Theory and Practice of Combining Management Science Methodologies*, ISBN 0471974900.

Morey, A.M. (2002). *Quantum Mechanics and Determinism: An Investigation into Gerard 't Hooft's Recent Theories*, http://physics.brown.edu/physics/undergradpages/theses/seniorthesis_morey.pdf.

Poundstone, W. (1985). *The Recursive Universe: Cosmic Complexity and the Limits of Scientific Knowledge*, ISBN 0688039758.

Price, H. (1992). "Metaphysical pluralism," *The Journal of Philosophy*, 89(8): 387-409.

Reschke, C.H. (2001). "Evolutionary perspectives on simulations of social systems," *Journal of Artificial Societies and Social Simulation*, 4(4), http://www.soc.surrey.

ac.uk/JASSS/4/4/8.html.

Richardson, K.A. (2001). "On the status of natural boundaries: A complex systems perspective," *Proceedings of the Systems in Management 7th Annual ANZSYS Conference 2001*, pp. 229-238, ISBN 072980500X.

Richardson, K.A. (2004a). "On the relativity of recognizing the products of emergence and the nature of physical hierarchy," conference paper presented at the *Second Biennial International Seminar on the Philosophical, Epistemological and Methodological Implications of Complexity Theory*, January 7-10th 2004, Havana, Cuba.

Richardson, K.A. (2004b). "The problematization of existence: Towards a philosophy of complexity," *Nonlinear Dynamics, Psychology, and the Life Sciences*, 8(1): 17-40.

Richardson, K.A. (2005). "Simplifying Boolean networks," *Advances in Complex Systems*, 8(4): 365-381.

Richardson, K.A. (2007). "From complicated to complex: On the relationship between connectivity and behavior," *Emergence: Complexity & Organization*, 9(1-2): 194-206.

Richardson, K.A. (2008). "On the limits of agent-based computer simulation: Towards a nonlinear modeling culture," in L. Dennard, K.A. Richardson and G. Morçöl (eds.), *Complexity and Policy Analysis: Tools and Concepts for Designing Robust Policies in Complex World*, ISBN 9780981703220, pp. 37-53.

Richardson, K.A. (2009). "Complexity, information and robustness: The role of information 'barriers' in Boolean networks," *Complexity*, 15(3): 26-42.

Richardson, K.A., Cilliers, P. and Lissack, M.R. (2001). "Complexity science: A 'gray' science for the 'stuff in between'," *Emergence*, 3(2): 6-18.

Richardson, K.A., Mathieson, G., and Cilliers, P. (2009). "Complexity thinking and military operational analysis," in K.A. Richardson (ed.), *Knots, Lace and Tartan: Making Sense of Complex Systems in Military Operations Research*, ISBN 9780981703244, pp. 27-69.

Sellars, R.W. (1927). "What is the correct interpretation of critical realism?" *The Journal of Philosophy*, 24(9): 238-241.

Shweder, R.A. (2001). "A polytheistic conception of the sciences and the virtues of deep variety," in A.R. Damasio, A. Harrington, J. Kagan, B.S. McEewn, H. Moss, and R. Shaikh (eds.), *Unity of Knowledge: The Convergence of Natural and Human Sciences*, ISBN 1573313114.

Sommerer, J.C. and Ott, E. (1993). "A physical system with qualitatively uncertain dynamics," *Nature*, 365(9 September): 138-140.

Stewart, I. and Cohen, J. (1997). *Figments of Reality*, Cambridge University Press: UK, ISBN 0521571553.

Tegmark, M. (1998). "Is 'the theory of everything' merely the ultimate ensemble theory?" *Annals of Physics*, 270: 1-51, http://arxiv.org/PS_cache/gr-qc/

pdf/9704/9704009v2.pdf.

Toffoli, T. (1984). "Cellular automata as an alternative to (rather than an approximation of) differential equations in modeling physics," *Physica D*, 10: 117-127.

't Hooft, G. (2002). "Determinism beneath quantum mechanics," arXiv, http://arxiv.org/PS_cache/quant-ph/pdf/0212/0212095v1.pdf.

van Gigch, J.P. (1991). *System Design Modeling and Metamodeling*, Plenum Press, New York: NY.

Vennix, J.A.M. (1996). *Group Model Building: Facilitating Team Learning Using System Dynamics*, ISBN 0471953555.

Wagner, A. (1999). "Causality in complex systems," *Biology and Philosophy*, 14: 83-101.

Wolfram, S. (1985). "Undecidability and intractability in theoretical physics," *Physical Review Letters*, 54(8): 735-738.

Wolpert, D.H. (2001). "Computational capabilities of physical systems," *Physical Review E*, 64: 016128, http://www.santafe.edu/media/workingpapers/96-03-008.pdf.

Wuensche, A. (1999). "Classifying cellular automata automatically: Finding gliders, filtering, and relating space-time patterns, attractor basins, and the z parameter," *Complexity*, 4(3): 47-66.

Wuensche, A. and Lesser, M.J. (1992). *The Global Dynamics of Cellular Automata, Santa Fe Studies in the Sciences of Complexity*, ISBN 0201557401.

ABOUT THE AUTHOR

Kurt A. Richardson is the owner of Emergent Publications (formerly ISCE Publishing), a publishing house that specializes in complexity-related publications, and is the CEO of Exploratory Solutions, a small company set-up to develop software to support decision making in complex environments. Kurt also designs and develops digital signal processing circuits for Orbital Network Engineering, and was a Senior Systems Engineer for NASA's Gamma-Ray Large Area Telescope (now Fermi). He is also developing Smart Energy products for use in the domestic home. He has a BSc(hons) in Physics (1992), MSc in Astronautics and Space Engineering (1993) and a PhD in Applied Physics (1996). Kurt's current research interests include the philosophical implications of assuming that everything we observe is the result of complex underlying processes, the relationship between structure and function, analytical frameworks for intervention design, and robust methods of reducing complexity, which have resulted in the publication of over thirty journal papers and book chapters, and ten books. He is the Managing/Production Editor for the international journal *Emergence: Complexity & Organization* and is on the review board for the journals *Systemic Practice and Action Research*, *Systems Research and Behavioral Science*, and *Tamara: Journal of Critical Postmodern Organization Science*.

LaVergne, TN USA
27 April 2010
180621LV00004B/3/P